MW00943240

RIDING
WITH MY DAD

Dr. Ninja

Riding With My Dad
By Dr. Ninja ™

Hadrcover ISBN 978-1-954192-00-3
Paperback ISBN 978-1-954192-02-7
Ebook ISBN 978-1-954192-01-0

Cover design by
Interior design by Amie McCracken

To Lana and our four children: Seth, Jared, Kenan, and Sarah.

Special shout out to everyone who has a veterinarian for a parent.

Table of Contents

Chapter 1
Bulldog Babies

The door! Hurry up, shut off the flashlight, head out from under the covers, now relax and breathe nice and even. In and out. They'd never know I wasn't asleep.

"Ray. Ray, wake up." Dad shook my shoulder. "Do you want to go help me do a C-section on Mrs. Jones's bulldog, Beauty? She went into labor early, and Mrs. Jones is in a panic."

"Sure, Dad."

I went downstairs, and Dad, already in his scrubs, waited in the kitchen, tapping his fingers on the counter. "Good book?"

Booked, literally, my shoulders slumped. "Yeah, I'm almost finished and couldn't wait until tomorrow."

"I never should have told you kids that I read under the covers, but I didn't tell you my secret for not getting caught." He gave me a wink, went into the garage, and hopped into his truck. I had to move a few things over so I would have a place to sit, but I was still sitting on some ropes and towels. The truck had coats, coveralls, boots, health papers, and all sorts of stuff in the front and back seats. It had an aroma of cow and horse manure along with a medicine smell. We drove through town, and it was quiet except for the two bars at the opposite ends of Main Street. People were out smoking in front of the West End Tap and a lot of people were sitting around talking outside the El Dorado.

"What book are you reading?"

"*My Friend Flicka*."

"An oldie but a goodie, one of my favorites."

"Grandpa Morrison gave it to me. He said that Great Grandpa and Grandma Morrison gave it to him for his birthday."

"He knew you would treasure it. It was one of his favorite books and you can pass it along to someone that will appreciate it."

A car was parked in front of the clinic, and a ginormously swollen bulldog on a leash sat next to a girl. A little woman peered through the front door with her hands on either side of her face and her nose stuck to the glass.

"I told you she was in a panic, didn't I?" said Dad as we drove around the back of the clinic and pulled into the garage. "It's too bad so many bull-dogs can't have their puppies on their own. It's the price you pay for 'beauty' I guess. Pun intended."

I rolled my eyes. Dad had such a strange sense of humor at times.

Dad nodded at me. "Surgery."

I walked through the clinic turning on lights. Gladys, the technician, had everything in its place so it was easy to find everything. Dogs started barking in the kennels when they heard the bell on the front door ring. They thought they were getting company and it was chow time. I was glad the clinic had as much soundproofing as it did or we wouldn't be able to hear a thing.

I was just attaching the tubes and rebreathing bag to the anesthetic machine when I heard Mrs. Jones's short, quick steps coming toward me. She burst around the door. "Ray, it's so good of you to come down and help with Beauty. I don't know what I would do if something happened to the puppies. I'm so glad I could reach your dad at this time of night. She only had four last time, and she'll probably have about that many again. She's so swollen she looks like she could have twenty, oh my poor little darling. My pretty, little dog is losing her figure."

She finally came up for air and set her puppy box down on the counter. She unrolled her heating pad cord and plugged it into the wall. She took towels, a turkey baster, gloves, zip ties, and a bunch more stuff out of the box. Mrs. Jones always reminded me of a wren—a little brown bird constantly flitting around and making a lot of noise in our back yard.

I heard a snuffling sound, and Beauty waddled around the corner with the girl holding the leash. Dad was behind her with an armful of supplies. Beauty was snorting through her smushed up nose, and her tongue was hanging out. She had stuff dripping out of her rear, leaving a gross green trail as she walked. She came up and sat next to me, leaned against my leg, and looked up to be petted. She was pretty, in an ugly sort of way.

"Ray, this is my granddaughter, Tori. She's staying with me this weekend so she could help me with Beauty's pups. Dr. Morrison, we're early enough aren't we? The puppies are going to be ok aren't they?" Mrs. Jones took off her glasses and dabbed at the corners of her eyes.

"They should be fine. You said she just started an hour ago didn't you? It can take several hours for a dog to have puppies so we should be in good shape." He was laying out supplies and hooking up the IV bag while he reassured Mrs. Jones.

"Are you ready, Ray?"

I nodded. He stooped over and picked up Beauty. His face turned red and the veins stood out on his neck. He straightened up and swung Mrs. Jones's "pretty, little dog" onto the table, then stood there and took a few breaths. "Ray, leg."

I knew Dad was not looking forward to this. Beauty had short legs with thick skin so it was hard to see a vein sometimes. I heard him muttering under his breath as he looked at the leg while he shaved it. Mrs. Jones hovered around, trying to get a good view of everything we did, telling us all about what a wonderful dog Beauty was. She then launched into a description of the father of the puppies and how he should have won Drake University's, Beautiful Bulldog Contest. Dad scrubbed the leg up and picked up the catheter. Tori just stood to the side and watched.

"Are you ready, Ray?" I nodded, closed my eyes, and put a death grip on the leg. What if Beauty jerked and Dad poked my thumb? That would really hurt. I couldn't let a girl see that I was afraid of needles let alone have Dad see.

"Ray. Ray, let go with your thumb. Ray!"

I relaxed and opened my eyes as Dad went into fast forward. He was a blur as he taped the catheter and hooked up the fluids.

He picked up the syringe of anesthetic, and I closed my eyes as he injected it into the catheter. I felt Beauty slump down, so I opened my eyes. Dad already had the endotracheal, or breathing tube, ready in his hand. I held her mouth open and pulled out her slimy tongue with a piece of gauze while he put the tube in. Even her tongue was ginormous. It was so thick and wide, it was no wonder it hung out all of the time. Dad soon had her tied down on her back and was shaving up her belly.

"Scrub."

Mrs. Jones stood there with a mask on her face, a

towel in one hand, and a zip tie in her other hand. She had given a mask and towel to Tori also.

I took the scrub over to Beauty and started scrubbing. Dad's very particular about it, and I had practiced several times before he would trust me. He always said prevention was better than treatment. Dad backed into the room and looked at what I had done.

"Three times?"

"Yes, Dad," I said, but was thinking, you would think I knew what I was doing by now wouldn't you? I am twelve after all.

He came over with his gloves on, put drapes on Beauty, and picked up the scalpel. He looked at the monitor and the bag moving with Beauty's breathing. "Ready?"

Mrs. Jones and Tori both nodded, then he cut down the middle of her stomach leaving it wide open with her insides showing. He pulled the purple uterus up, made an incision, and started gently squeezing the uterus until he milked out a puppy. He clamped the umbilical cord and pulled on it until the gross, green placenta came out, then dropped the puppy into the towel in Mrs. Jones's hand. She started rubbing the puppy, set it on the counter, put a zip tie around the umbilical cord, and then cut the umbilical cord. She took the turkey baster and sucked fluids out of the puppy's mouth. I saw her doing that out of the corner of my eye as Dad was already dropping a puppy onto the towel in my hand. We worked like an assembly line as Dad milked out a puppy, dropped it in the towel I was holding, then I handed it to Tori, and she took it to Mrs. Jones. The first puppy was already squealing by the time I handed off the third.

Dad finally leaned back, stretching, and looked at me. "That's the last puppy. Did we have five?"

"Yes, that's five. The fourth puppy isn't breathing yet." Mrs. Jones held up a sticky green and brown puppy.

Dad nodded. "Ray, why don't you give it a little artificial respiration. Put the medicine under the tongue to make it breath first."

I picked up the syringe with the medicine in it and felt a bit woozy. The beef stick I had eaten before bed thought it wanted to come back up. I just stood there swaying, looking at the needle with the cap on it. I couldn't be a wuss and faint in front of a girl. What would Dad think of me?

"Ray, just unscrew the needle. You've done that before. Get moving!"

I closed my eyes, unscrewed the needle cap, and dropped the needle on the floor. No needle now, so much better. I put a drop of medicine under the puppy's tongue. I started blowing lightly into its open mouth and nose and working its little body back and forth. I could still see the heart beating in its chest, so I knew it was alive. Mrs. Jones was working with the other puppies, but I could see her looking over her shoulder. Tori stared at me, her face worried. I rubbed it some more with the towel and kept trying to breath into its open mouth while Dad sewed up Beauty. He gave me a smile and an encouraging nod, so I kept blowing and working it to try to get it to breathe. Finally, there was a little gasp and then a squeal. The puppy started taking big breaths and squirming in the towel, squealing louder.

"Oh, you wonderful boy, you saved Beauty's puppy," gushed Mrs. Jones as she took the puppy. "It's a boy, so I'm going to name it Ray since you saved his life. Tori, didn't Ray do a good job?"

Tori hugged me and whispered in my ear, "That was wonderful. You saved the puppy."

I felt my face getting hot so I turned to Dad. "Is there anything else you need now Dad?"

He smiled. "No, I'm doing just fine. See what you can do to help Mrs. Jones."

Mrs. Jones had all five puppies in the puppy box with an electric heating pad under the blanket. They were squirming around bumping into each other, nuzzling around for their mother and something to eat.

"Aren't they just adorable, Tori?" Mrs. Jones took off her mask and had a smile from one ear to the other. "There are three girls and two boys. The light brown one with the spot on top of his head is Ray."

Dad was about done sewing up Beauty. "Ray,

turn off the anesthetic but leave the oxygen the way it is." He put in one final stitch, pulled his gloves off, and loosened everything holding the breathing tube in place. "I'll start cleaning up while you watch Beauty. Pull the tube if she starts coughing."

Dad carried the surgical instruments out for Gladys to finish cleaning and sterilizing in the morning. Beauty lay there peacefully breathing, sound asleep, not even aware she was a mother. The monitor was beeping, the puppies were squealing, and Mrs. Jones talked about Beauty and how wonderful she and the puppies were.

"Ray, let's put Beauty in a cage until she wakes up completely. That won't take very long."

I knew that Dad was taking the heavy end, but Beauty still weighed a ton when I picked up my half. Dad backed into the kennel room where he had left the door open to a kennel with a grate. The three dogs in the kennels all perked up and looked at us, even Lucky, the dog Dad had done surgery on to fix his leg that afternoon. Mrs. Jones followed us all the way with the mop and cleaned up anything that dripped out of Beauty's back end. She was an old pro at this, even if she was a worrywart.

Dad turned off the light as we left the kennel. "We'll leave the light off now so Beauty can wake up where it is nice and quiet. I'll finish cleaning up while we're waiting."

Mrs. Jones went back to fussing over the puppies. "Tori, I wish your Grandfather Mark, were here to see the puppies. He so enjoyed raising them and hated to sell them." She took off her glasses and started dabbing at her eyes again.

She started sniffing, so I ran and picked up a box of tissues to hand to her.

"Thank you, Ray. Here, just a second, I think I have my purse here." She rummaged around in her pile of stuff on the counter and turned around with a $20 bill in her hand. "Here, this is for you."

"Thanks, Mrs. Jones. You don't need to give me anything."

"You keep it. This here pup, Ray, wouldn't be alive if it wasn't for you."

I heard toenails clicking on the floor, and Beauty came into the room with Dad. She was a little wobbly but alert. Mrs. Jones set the puppy box on the floor, and Beauty started licking the puppies and making snorting sounds.

"Isn't she wonderful?" said Mrs. Jones for the umpteenth time. "Let's go home Beauty."

She picked up the box of puppies, and Beauty followed behind. Beauty's sides were sunken in, and she was only two thirds as big as she had been when she came in. Dad, Tori, and I picked up all of Mrs. Jones's other stuff and took it out to her car. Mrs. Jones set the puppies in the back seat, and Beauty hopped up with a little assistance from Dad. She was nuzzling and snuffling over the pups crying for milk.

"Thanks again, Dr. Morrison, and you too Ray. I'll see you soon. It won't be long until it's time for the puppies' vaccinations. Tori's going to stay with me this summer. Maybe she can come to the clinic and job shadow you since she wants to be a vet? Ray, you can show her around the fair too."

"I'm sure we can work out something."

"Wonderful," she said and closed her door.

"Well, Ray, it's not every day you have a dog named after you. You earned it though."

"Thanks, Dad." I was thinking that I hoped I would never have to give a shot. I wondered if Dad had noticed I was scared? I didn't think Tori noticed.

Dad locked up, and we went home. The people were still talking outside the El Dorado, and the others were still smoking at the West End Tap. The house was quiet when we went into the kitchen, and the next morning I didn't even remember going to bed.

Chapter 2
The Running of the Bulls

Matt Schrage stood next to the chute holding the bull's tail while Dad measured the bull. Dad stood up and peered at the measuring tape.

Matt looked expectantly at Dad. "What's he measure, Doc?"

"Thirty-nine centimeters plus. He's a good one."

"Great, I've him sold to that movie star, Johnny Deters. He liked the bulls I had at the beef expo, so he came down with his farm manager and bought these two at the farm. Celebrities make for good advertising when you're trying to sell bulls. It's my chance to really do something with the farm."

"Matt, it always amazes me how people in this little town of Clifton get to meet people like that. They say you're only six handshakes away from anyone in the world, and it does seem true. I met someone that just shook hands with the Queen of England the day before I talked to him. Ok, let's just make sure this bull can sire some prize-winning calves."

Dad had Matt hold the tail to keep the probe in and collected a sample from the bull. "That looks like a good one, Matt. I'll go take a look at it under the microscope."

He put a couple of drops on a warm slide and stained one. He put coverslips on them, sat down at the microscope, and dialed down to low power while he focused up and down. "They sure are swimming well, very good motility. Let's see what kind of quality there is," Dad said as he moved the slide over and switched to high power. "Everything looks pretty good, a few abnormal ones, but they all have that. Do you want to take a look?"

"Yeah, I want to see them." Matt slid into the seat.

"It's easier if you look through only one eye since I have it set for my eyes. Do you see a lot of little tadpoles swimming around?"

"Doc, how can you tell what anything is with all that swirling round?"

"It just takes practice, here, I'll move it over so you can see the stained ones I killed. It should be easier to see individual cells then."

"They do look a lot like tadpoles when they aren't moving."

"Let's vaccinate and deworm this bull and check the other one." Dad slapped Matt on the back. "It looks like you'll be hobnobbing with movie stars."

The other bull passed with flying colors too. Dad vaccinated him and let him out into the pen with the other bull.

"Are you ready to load 'em, Matt?"

"Yeah, I'll hold the trailer gate." And he opened the door to the outside. "I'm ready, let 'em go."

Dad opened the door and gate, then waved at the bulls, hissing at them to get them to move. They turned and ran for the open door. They both tried to get out at once and couldn't fit. They pushed and shoved until one bull backed off and the other bull squirted out the door. Dad waved at the bull that was left, and he jumped out the door. I heard the other bull's feet in the trailer already, then I looked out the door as Matt started to swing the gate shut. The first bull had turned around and started butting heads with the second bull as he tried to get on the trailer. He swung around and hit the gate, knocking Matt to the ground.

Dad yelled, "Matt, get up or you'll get tromped!"

Matt rolled over toward us and stood up. We watched helplessly as the bulls continued fighting. The bulls were shoving each other back and forth, their heads held low. Then the first bull shoved really hard and came out of the trailer. Dirt was flying, and the bulls were bellowing as first one then the other gained advantage. They moved off to the side, and the door swung shut on the trailer. The second bull was being butted in the side when he saw the opening where the trailer gate had been and took off on the run between the trailer and the side of the clinic with the other bull in hot pursuit to the back yard of the clinic.

Dad directed Matt. "Go get on the other side of the trailer so they don't go out into the street. Ray, come with me and grab a sorting stick to wave."

We went running through the garage grabbing sorting sticks and sprinted to the front of the clinic. "Gladys, Sue, the bulls are loose. We have to corral them and run them back into the clinic."

A look of panic came over Sue's face, but Gladys just came running along. We ran out the front door and around the clinic to the back. The bulls were contentedly cropping the newly mown grass in the back; the fighting was over for now. The lumberyard behind the clinic had a chain link fence so we had the bulls surrounded. Sue came up behind Gladys, peering around her at the bulls.

"Matt, stand in front of the truck and don't let them get around you. We'll try to ease them back along the building and into the clinic. Ray, just stand there and move when I tell you to. Hold out your stick to the side so you look bigger than you are. Don't wave it or you'll just scare them. Gladys, stand between Ray and me. Sue, go back in and call the police. Tell them what's going on. Tell them not to come here fast or with the lights or sirens on. Ok, if they come at you, get out of the way, don't take a chance on being hurt."

Dad started easing forward toward the bulls,

talking softly, "Ok boys, let's turn around and go back into the clinic. That's the way, that's the right thing to do."

The bulls lifted their heads when Dad started talking to them. Gladys held her hands out to her sides and took a step toward the bulls. The bulls slowly turned and started walking back to the gap between the trailer and the clinic. We eased forward, making a human fence around them and kept them slowly moving. They reached the gap between the truck and clinic and one bull started into the gap. The other bull rammed him from behind and the fight was back on. The lead bull turned, and they squared off head to head. The bulls were pushing and shoving, kicking gravel up. Crunch! The side of Matt's truck caved in as a bull's rear end swung into it. Bang! They hit the side of the clinic and a dent appeared in the metal siding, but the wall stayed up.

Dad wiped his face. "I'm glad that wall's made of concrete, otherwise we'd have had another real mess. Back off, and they'll quit fighting soon."

Gladys and I stepped back. One bull finally conceded defeat and backed off. They started eating grass again like nothing had happened.

"Ray, go in and open the overhead garage door to give them a bigger opening to go in. Move the stuff out of the way first, and make sure all of the other doors are closed. Matt, pull your truck ahead and to the side so the bulls have a bigger opening to go through. Get ready to run to the back to stop them from getting on the street. Gladys and I will hold them here until you're ready."

Sue was frozen to her seat inside as I ran through the clinic. I slammed the door shut as I ran into the garage and weaved my way to the garage door opener. The door started up, and I was moving things out of the way, making as wide of a path to the pens for the bulls as I could. I saw the trailer moving as the door went up. I ran out the front door as a cop car pulled up.

Bob Peters opened the car door. "Have you corralled the bulls yet?"

"Nope, we almost had them, but they started fighting again. I opened the garage door so they'll have more room to come back into the garage. Dad's around the back. Follow me."

Bob went with me. "Doc, when did you start having rodeos? I'm sure you could charge people to watch bull riding."

Dad didn't take his eyes off the bulls. "You'll have to ask Matt if you want to ride one. They belong to Johnny Deters, so it's celebrity bull riding. Bob, you go over on the other side of Gladys and we'll work them slowly back into the clinic. Ray, you just hang back and make sure you don't get run over and fill in a gap as needed."

Dad held up his stick and the bulls turned, knowing the drill by now. They slowly started moving toward the dented truck. This time they didn't even make it there before one bellowed and they started fighting again. They shoved each other back and forth, twisting their heads, trying to gain an advantage on the other bull. Chunks of sod flew as their hooves cut up the yard.

"Get back everyone, don't get hurt!" Dad yelled.

It seemed like they would keep this up all day; they didn't seem to be getting tired. One of the bulls finally backed off and turned to move away. The other bull hit him in the side and that caused him to take off trying to get away. He ran at the fence to the lumberyard and reared up, trying to jump the fence. He was like a whale rising out of the ocean, except he landed on the chain link fence. The fence collapsed as a pole broke off with him astraddle the chain link. He wiggled on over into the lumberyard. The other bull came up grunting and bellowing and hopped the broken fence with ease.

The noise had attracted the attention of the guys working in the lumberyard. They stood in the yard watching the whole thing. The bulls trotted toward the open door of the lumber shed, kicking up dust as they went. The doors were open on both ends of the shed, and Dad was yelling for them to shut the door to the street. We had followed the bulls into the lumberyard and could see the bulls now in the shed, heading for the open door at the other end and freedom.

Big John, a guy that worked at the lumberyard,

was suddenly silhouetted in the open door at the other end of the shed just as the bulls arrived at the door. We heard a scream and he was gone, diving to the side and out of sight. Dad and I were running as fast as we could behind the bulls to shut the door behind them at our end, but the black bulls suddenly burst into sunlight and were totally loose. I could hear Bob Peters behind me shouting that he was going to head them off with his car. Matt was cussing up a blue streak behind us.

We ran out into the street, and Peewee Smith watched Big John dust himself off from his dive to get away from the bulls. We stood with our hands on our knees, trying to catch our breath. The bulls were munching on the grass by the railroad track.

Dad stood up. "The door at the other end and of the shed is shut so we'll try to run them back into the shed. We can use a few of the gates they sell here and load them up out of the shed."

Pewee Smith and Big John went across the street to try and turn the bulls back. Dad and I went to one side and Matt went to the other. Bob Peters came roaring around the corner in his car. The bulls took one look at the car and started down the railroad tracks toward the north end of town.

Matt started running to try and circle around them and head them back to the shed, but the bulls just started moving faster, breaking into a trot. Matt stopped and held his side as Dad and

I caught up to him. I heard tires screeching, and Bob Peters was heading the other direction in his car now. The bulls reached the VFW and started munching on the lawn at the edge of the tracks. They were puffing a little now, their sides heaving. We walked down the tracks toward them, and they paid no attention as we weren't a threat.

Dad stopped. "Let's circle around them and head them back down the tracks and see if we can get them in the shed.

We waded through the weeds on the side of the tracks and into the grass with the bulls, when we heard a train whistle as the train approached the first crossing in town.

Dad turned. "Hurry up, get them away from the tracks so they aren't hit by the train! Take them toward town."

We ran, yelling at the bulls, their heads already up, ears pricked and eyes wide open looking in the direction of the whistle. They had never been anywhere near a train before. The ground started to shake as the engine came into sight. The bulls launched themselves toward town to get away from the terror coming at them. They went across the street and down an alley with Dad and Matt in pursuit. The bulls both slowed down as the train rumbled along behind us, men and bulls both winded.

A woman was putting clothes on her clothesline in her backyard. She looked up and threw the basket away and started jumping up and down. "It's a bull; it's a bull, and I'm wearing red. It's a bull, and I'm wearing red!" The bulls just stared at her in amazement.

I had caught up by now and heard Dad muttering under his breath, "Helen, they're colorblind." He then said with a firm voice, "Helen, be quiet, they're more scared of you than you of them, though it's hard to believe. They're colorblind. Just step back into your house."

She was trembling but did what Dad said. The bulls were standing with their heads hanging low; they had not run this far in a long time or maybe ever. More people were showing up after they heard about the excitement on the police scanner. Bob Peters pulled up behind us.

"Bob, take Ray around to the other end of the alley and block off the street. We will bring the bulls up the alley slowly and then you can turn them into the bank drive-through. We can block off both ends and load them out of there. The trailer should fit perfectly."

Bob nodded and I hopped into the front seat of the car with him. We went whipping around the corner, and Bob pulled around the block, stopping the police car at an angle to herd the bulls toward the drive-through. The bulls were coming nice and slow up the alley now, and I stood there with my sorting stick. The bulls started to turn toward the driveway as I held out my sorting stick.

I was going to be the hero that corralled the bulls. I would have my picture on the front page of the paper and everything. A car pulled ahead out of the drive-through right then. The driver stared at me with a quizzical look on his face and then turned to see what I was looking at. He saw the bulls coming at him and laid on his horn and wouldn't stop honking.

The blaring horn gave the bulls new energy. They whirled around and about knocked me over trying to get away from this new terror. They went flying across the street and into the alley in the next block. Now a half dozen people were in hot pursuit. Matt was about in tears as he and Dad came up.

Dad was yelling, "Stop chasing them! Stop chasing them!"

The people were soon winded and stopped chasing the bulls as they heard Dad. The bulls slowed down then and were just plodding along.

Bob said, "Get in, and we'll head them off."

Dad, Matt, and I all climbed into the car and headed down toward Main Street. We turned on Main Street. It was full of cars and people gawking, trying to see what the excitement was. The retired farmers stood outside the café with coffee cups in their hands, their morning confab disturbed. A car was backing out, and we had to wait for it since we didn't want to make a lot of noise and scare the bulls again. I could see Bob nervously chomping his gum, anxious to be moving again. Matt was in the front seat, leaning ahead, trying to see if the bulls were in sight yet. Bob put his lights on now and people scattered out of our way. The alley curved around to Main Street and went under the viaduct. Bob slewed the car around, past the opening of the alley, and we piled out.

The bulls came around the curve of the alley, and now, there was no place for them to go but Main Street. A half dozen people were following them at a distance. Dad held up his hand, and they stopped. A few of the people out smoking in front of the West End Tap started directing traffic, using exaggerated gestures, waving people on one direction and stopping people coming our way. The bulls stepped onto Main Street and stopped, bewildered as to what to do now.

They didn't have to make a decision though as a semi came down Main Street hill behind us with his air brakes on, trying to slow down quickly. The loud BUM, BUM, BUM, echoed under the viaduct, amplifying the noise. The bulls were on the move again, down Main Street this time. Both sides of the street were full of cars so there was really nowhere for them to go except down Main Street. They were so tired, they were moving slowly, and we followed behind them on foot with Bob behind us in the car, lights flashing.

We went right past the Clifton Gazette office. Ivan, the owner, was out front with a camera, snapping away. "Say cheese, Doc," he chortled. The flash from the camera didn't faze the bulls as they plodded along.

The farmers, their coffee cups in hand, had formed a curved line at the intersection at the end of the block. The bulls obediently turned as they reached them and went down the hill toward the clinic. We started walking along closer now, about even with their back legs, Matt on one side and Dad with me on the other. "The bulls will keep walking if you stay there." The bulls kept plodding along now, heads low, foam dripping from their mouths. A large crowd was now following, and Ivan was taking more pictures. Police Chief Bill Digger had his car pulled across the road to block traffic by the clinic and was standing next to the car with Gladys. They moved to the side and held their arms out. The bulls, well trained by now, turned and trotted to the safety of the clinic, walking through the open clinic garage door.

Matt, Dad, and I ran into the garage, and Dad hit the garage door opener. The chain rattled, and the door closed. The bulls were so tired that they stood there, their sides heaving. Dad and Matt both had red faces from running all over town.

Dad gave a big sigh. "You ready to try it again Matt?"

Matt nodded. "I'll back up the trailer and this time I'll wait until they are both on before I try to close the door. Let's get them a couple of buckets of water first since they're so hot."

I went to fill a couple of buckets while Matt went out. I could hear the diesel engine start and Dad went out to help guide him. The back gate to the trailer squealed as it opened. We herded the bulls back into the pens. Matt went out to hold the back gate of the trailer again. Dad slid the door open, and the bulls went to the daylight, going through the door single file this time. They jumped into the trailer, and Matt ran in and shut them into the front half of the trailer so they wouldn't have room to fight. Matt latched the back gate shut and put the clip on so it wouldn't accidentally open.

Dad took off his hooded sweatshirt, and his scrubs were soaked through. Matt had sweat stains under his arms, and his face was red with sweat dripping down it.

Both men looked at each other and then started laughing. "Did you see Helen Tangent jumping up and down and yelling about wearing red?"

"What about the guys from the tap directing traffic?"

"I don't think Sue will ever come back in the garage again."

"Big John must have thought the bull was bigger than him, so much for his glory days playing football."

"What do you think the train engineer thought?"

Matt suddenly turned serious. "I'm just glad we got them back and no one was hurt. This sale can really help me sell more bulls. I just don't need any publicity about them getting loose. That won't look good."

Dad shook his head. "It's too late for that, but I don't think Johnny Deters reads the Clifton Gazette, so you should be safe."

Matt shook his head in disgust. "I hope none of his pictures turn out." He hopped into the truck and pulled out with the bulls.

Chief Digger and Bob Peters were standing in the office and started laughing when they saw us. The chief said, "Let us know when you have your next rodeo. We can charge admission. Of course, you need to apply for a permit to hold one. Oh well, no one was hurt and insurance will take care of the damages."

Dad laughed too. "I'll try to let you know ahead of time if we have something like this again. I have to go wash up. See you later."

That Wednesday, the paper came out. The front page had a picture of the bulls walking down Main Street with me, Dad, and Matt behind. The headline read *The Running of the Bulls*. There was a big article and there were pictures of the farmers with their coffee cups and the crowd following the bulls. My friends at school were envious that they had missed all of the excitement. I didn't tell them how much hard work it had been and how scared I was when the bulls were fighting.

Chapter 3
Morel Mushroom Bonus

The ribs were like the poles on a tent, the skin sagged between them on the puppy's chest. It lay there with its chin on the exam table, dull eyes sunk back in the sockets, staring up woefully at me. The tail moved side to side ever so slightly as I looked at him. Dad, wearing exam gloves, was busy examining the puppy. He pulled up on the skin on the back of the neck, and it stayed standing up when he let go. Gladys, took the puppy's temperature while Dad checked the puppy's gums.

"Doc, that puppy was right as rain last night," said the owner, Six-Pack Krebs. "I gave it some gunpowder last week to deworm it, so he shouldn't have any worms. That's the only thing my dad ever used to deworm a dog, and he had a lot of dogs. I haven't given him that there Parvo shot from the feed store since he is only five months and has to be six months old to get that." He leaned over and spit in the trash can. "That there pup, Bud, means the world to my old lady, Doc. She's real sick, and he's the only real company that she gets when I'm working. Do whatever you can to save him, Doc."

Bud strained, and reddish brown stinking poop covered the table. Dad turned around. "Ray, go get a Parvo test out of the cooler."

I ran out to the laboratory and pulled a box from the cooler. I grabbed a swab and test kit and went back to the exam room. Gladys coated the swab with a sample of reddish diarrhea and started the test while Dad talked. The room reeked like something had died.

"Six-Pack, we usually vaccinate puppies three times for Distemper and Parvo starting at six weeks, so this puppy is three vaccinations behind already." Dad went through his usual talk with new puppy owners. He taught them about vaccinations, worms, heartworms, fleas, ticks, feeding and training a new puppy. He sounded like a salesman and teacher combined when he got going.

Gladys held the test up for Dad to see, and he sighed. "The test is positive, Six-Pack. Your puppy has Parvovirus, and it's expensive to treat. There's a chance he won't make it. We'll have to keep him here in isolation on IV fluids and other treatments for several days. He can go home when he starts eating."

Six-Pack leaned over the table and started breathing with his mouth open, and fumes filled the room. Now I understood why they called him "Six-Pack" and it was only ten in the morning on a Saturday. Tears rolled down his rosy-veined cheeks onto his straggly beard and then spattered onto the table. His body even started to shake.

"Doc, old buddy, I don't have that kind of money. Will you take payments?"

Dad gave another sigh. "Sue'll get a down payment and work out a payment plan with you. Gladys, take Bud back to isolation. Ray, clean and disinfect the room and the scale out front."

His tears started even heavier then as Six-Pack held out his hand. "Thanks, Doc. I really appreciate it. You know I'm good for it. I'll check back every day to see how he's doing." He continued pumping Dad's hand. "My old lady will sure appreciate it."

Gladys took Bud to the back while Dad led Six-Pack out front to Sue. I picked up the disinfectant spray and started spraying everywhere the puppy had been, plus everything Six-Pack had touched. Dad called his hands fomites—something that diseases will hitch a ride on to go infect something somewhere else. I overdid the disinfectant. My nose started to burn and tears came to my eyes. I opened the door to the exam room and hurriedly wiped up the disinfectant. Gladys would come back and do a more thorough job later.

Dad and Gladys already had an IV in and the fluids dripping before I even put on my booties and walked into the isolation area. Bud's tail started to wag as I walked into the room. He was feeling better already. Dad kept writing down the treatments Bud was going to get, and Gladys was filling syringes and giving injections. I was glad Gladys was here to do this. All those needles just gave me the willies.

Dad leaned over and looked at me. "Ray, you looked a lot like this pup once. You were vomiting and couldn't hold anything down. I came home from work, and you were gray. I was really worried, but I had so many emergency calls that I couldn't go with your mother, and she had to take you to the emergency room by herself. They kept you on IV fluids all night just like this puppy, and you were just fine the next morning."

It was hard to imagine this pitiful thing in front of me looking just fine ever, and especially not tomorrow. Suddenly, Bud raised his head and sat up, his sides started heaving, and he gagged up some yellow foamy stuff.

Dad was looking at me, a smile on his face. "It'll take longer than one night for this puppy to feel better. He'll look worse before he gets better, so get used to the smell. It seems a case like this always comes in on a Saturday morning so we have to take care of it all weekend."

I wrinkled up my nose in disgust. "Just what I wanted to do, Dad."

That night, we went down to the clinic. Dad

was right, a strong disgusting smell hit my nose when he opened the door to the room. Bud did look even more pitiful. The sides of the kennel had bloody diarrhea splashed on them and it left a trail as it had run down to the grate. We moved Bud out and hooked a new bag of fluids up. Then we heard a pounding coming from the front of the clinic. They were yelling and tapping on the glass too. Some people panic when they have a problem with an animal and go straight to the clinic without calling, never thinking that we don't live there.

"Go see who it is, Ray. I'll finish with Bud and be right up."

I took off my booties and smock and went up front and flipped on the outside lights. Six-Pack and two of his cronies were peering in through the window of the front door, smearing it with their hands and noses. I unlocked the front door, and Six-Pack came in, brushing past me before I could say anything. His cronies followed him, heading to the back of the clinic.

"I'm here to see Bud. I just couldn't stand having him down here all by himself. The old lady is so lonely at home all by herself. Max and Dick here want to see him too. Bud, where are you Bud?"

Dad came around the corner and staggered back a half step at the sight of the crowd bearing down on him. "Six-Pack we just settled Bud down for the night, and he's doing just fine. I can't let you go back and see him since he's in isolation. You would have to wear booties, a cap, gloves, and a gown, and I would have to charge you for all of it. Ray and I haven't had supper, and my wife has it waiting for us. I'll give you a call tomorrow morning about how he's doing."

"Come on, Doc. It'll just take a few minutes," he slurred and held up a bag. "Besides, I have his favorite treats for him. That'll get him eating if anything will."

Dad was firm. "I can't take the chance of you spreading Parvo to other animals. You don't want them to get sick, do you? I'll give you a call tomorrow morning. Ray and I'll be down in the morning before we go to church."

He shooed them toward the door and patted Six-Pack on the back. "We're doing the best we can for him. Do you want me to call you before or after we go to church?"

"Doc, you better call me after church and you eat dinner. I don't want to bother you too early."

Dad shut the door and locked it behind them and rolled his eyes ever so slightly. "They better hope they don't run into Bob Peters tonight. I didn't know if we would get them out of here tonight or not." I nodded every time he said something, since he was just venting.

"They must have been up at the West End Tap before they came here. The fumes were pretty strong, weren't they? He sure didn't want to be bothered too early tomorrow morning for being so concerned about Bud, did he? Let's go home and see what your mother has saved for us for supper."

The next morning Bud looked more pathetic, something I didn't think was possible. He still had what Dad called projectile diarrhea. The walls of the kennel were covered again. It was a good thing he was on a grate or he would have been covered in the stuff. He had some smeared on his side, and I started gagging as soon as the door was opened. He was thinner, if that was possible, and with all of that goo on him, I didn't want to touch him.

Dad just laughed at me. "I guess it's a good thing I don't have a good nose. Here, put on this smock, booties, and gloves. In five minutes, you won't even notice it anymore."

We hooked up a new bag of fluids, and Dad gave him all of his treatments. We washed him up some and put him in a clean kennel. He didn't smell too bad by then. My nose must have become numb or something. I couldn't smell a thing. Dad said if something really smells bad, don't leave and then come back, or your nose will have to get used to it all over again.

Chores were done, so Dad decided to call before church anyway, just to see if Six-Pack was up. Six-Pack lived in a house, or rather a cabin, over on the river. Most people just live in their cabins on weekends or on vacation in the summer since they are down a long muddy lane, but not Six-Pack. He's a true river rat—jon boat, catfishing, turtling, and all.

Dad called and talked for a while and finally hung up. "Guess old Six-Pack is asleep. Imagine that. Lois Krebs, though, is a very nice lady. She said she would tell Six-Pack how Bud is doing. She thanked me for what we are doing and said the pup means the world to Six-Pack."

"I thought he said Bud meant the world to her?"

He smiled. "Do you think a woman would name a puppy, Bud?"

Oh, it finally dawned on me. "Guys just can't get sentimental over an animal, can they?"

"Nope, they are often the worst when something bad happens to their animal. They just try to hide it."

Dad went down after church to treat Bud, and I went down again with him before supper. Bud looked just as pathetic as he had earlier, but there was only one splash of diarrhea on the wall. I wrinkled up my nose and tried to breathe through my mouth until I was used to it this time. Bud looked up at me and started to feebly wag his tail.

"Tomorrow will tell the tale." Dad gave Bud his treatments. "This'll be the turning point for him. Does he have enough energy left to get better is the question. He should start eating tomorrow if he's going to get better. It's a good thing he was a little older when he started getting sick."

We pulled out of the garage at the clinic and started down the street. A truck pulled up behind us and started honking and flashing its lights.

"Now what?" said Dad disgustedly as he pulled over and parked.

A rusted camouflaged pickup pulled up beside us. Max was driving, and Six-Pack was on the passenger side. He rolled down his window and hung his head out.

"Doc, I couldn't catch you at the clinic. How's Bud doing?"

"He's at the point where he is going to go downhill fast or get better. We'll know tomorrow how he's going to do."

"Thanks, Doc." He held a bag out the window and thrust it toward Dad. "Here's something until you're better paid. I'll check on him at the clinic in the morning."

He rolled up his window, and the truck rumbled as Max took off down the street and made a U-turn. Dad opened the package: mushrooms. Bonus! Fresh morel mushrooms for supper I hoped.

"I think your mother won't mind this kind of payment. I don't have enough time to go mushroom hunting so these are a real treat."

The next afternoon I pedaled down to the clinic after school. I had an unofficial job at the clinic. I liked going there, and Dad said if I hung out there, I needed to earn my keep. I came in the back door and headed for the isolation room and looked through the window. Bud was standing there, thinner than ever, but wagging his tail. He had the IV line all twisted up from turning around.

I heard a voice behind me. "Why don't you get him some fresh food and water? If he eats, he'll be ready to go home. He hasn't eaten anything or drank yet today."

"Ok, Dad."

I went to the storage area and found the best tasting can of puppy food I could find. I put two spoonfuls in a bowl and went back to isolation. I put on my booties, gown, and gloves; opened the door; and offered it to Bud. He sniffed at it, kind of licked it, gagged a little, and went, "Urp."

"It looks like he's not ready to eat yet. His stomach's too upset," said Dad. "He'll probably eat by morning and then he can go home."

We took off all of the stuff and headed up front. There was Six-Pack at the front counter. "How is he, Doc?" He hefted a bag up onto the counter. "First radishes of the year, just pulled them this morning."

Dad picked up the bag. "He's doing a lot better but isn't ready to eat. I think he'll be ready to go home tomorrow. We'll also get him dewormed and started on heartworm preventive too. That is, if he eats and drinks."

"Thanks, Doc, I really 'ppreciate it. I'll be back tomorrow." Six-Pack went out the door, spit tobacco juice, then stuck his head back in the door.

"I'll bring you some more mushrooms tomorrow. They're really coming on now." The bell over the door tinkled as it shut. Max was in his truck and fired it up as Six-Pack climbed in, and then they rumbled out of the parking lot.

"We're getting some really good things to eat at least. I don't know how much money we'll get. He usually pays sometime, but at least we'll eat well. Sue, Gladys, do you want any of these?"

Both of them said yes and went to get containers to divvy up the goodies. There's nothing like something fresh out of the garden.

The next afternoon I raced to the clinic to see Bud. I hurried back to isolation, but it was empty. I had rushed for nothing. I didn't even get to say goodbye to Bud. At least it didn't smell now except for the disinfectant.

Gladys came up to me and said, "Bud ate and drank this morning, and Six-Pack couldn't wait to get him home to his wife." She held up her hands and made quotation marks as she said wife. "I have some mushrooms for you to take home to your mother. Your dad's out on a call now and won't be back before we close. I guess you're lucky since I've already cleaned up all of the kennels."

She gave me a wink and handed me a bag. I missed Bud, but at least we would have something good to eat again tonight, and Mom would be happy. I thought that was the last of it, but

Six-Pack stopped in all summer and dropped off something to eat from his garden or the river. Mom didn't care to fix the turtle though.

Chapter 4
Ivory

"Ivory, should have her calf tonight or tomorrow morning," said Dad. "I know I've been saying that she should have it any time now for over a week, but this time she has really changed." Dad pointed. "See how she has loosened up on either side of her tailhead, and she has that big string of mucus coming out now. Remember how her calf was kicking and you could see the feet poking her right side last week?"

"Yep, can we stay and watch?"

"Ray, it's ten o'clock now and you have school tomorrow morning. She might not have it until four in the morning. She should be ok; it's not like this is her first calf. I'll come out first thing in the morning and check her before I do anything else."

We headed back to the truck, walking through the rest of the cows. "What do you think she'll have, a bull or a heifer? I hope it's a heifer, then I can show her and her calf at the fair and at the World Beef Expo this fall. Will it be a red point or a black point like her?"

"She'll have what she'll have. We bred her to Strut so she should have a good calf. Her calf from last year, Snow Queen, is a good heifer for you to show at the fair this year."

I looked back at Ivory as we came to the truck. The moon was almost full, and I could see her silhouetted against the night sky. She was standing there, hunched with her tail up in the air. The other cows were contentedly chewing their cuds in the moonlight, swishing their tails and staring at us. They were all old show cows and didn't have the least bit of fear of us. My other two American British White Park cows just about glowed in the moonlight with their white coats set off by the black noses, ears, and eyes. Dad started the truck, so I climbed in and we went home.

Mom called out when we walked through the door, "Has she had her calf yet? The girls waited but had to get to bed for school tomorrow."

"No, Mom, but tonight or tomorrow she should have it."

Mom raised an eyebrow. "That's what your dad's been saying for over a week."

"This time it's different, Mom. She has bloody mucus, and she's standing hunched up with her tail in the air."

"Ok, I believe you this time. Get to bed now, it's late. I'll get you up in the morning, but you can sleep in a bit."

The next morning I heard the phone ring and jumped out of bed. Mom called up the steps, "Ray, it's your dad."

I jumped over the last three steps and hit the rug at the bottom. It skidded across the floor, dropping me on my rear. I scrambled up and ran to the kitchen.

I grabbed the phone out of Mom's hand. "Did he say what it was?"

She gave me a funny look and walked out of the kitchen. I put the phone to my ear. "What did she have Dad? Is it a bull or a heifer?"

"Well Ray, she had it, and it's a bull, but it's dead. His head was a little swollen with his tongue sticking out. He wasn't that big, so he must have had a leg bent a little or something so she had trouble having him. I guess I should've gone out during the night and checked her. I might have been able to save him if I did that, but you never know for sure."

"Oh," was all I could say over the lump in my throat.

"I have to go to work now and have a busy day. I'll pick you up after work and we can bury the calf tonight. We'll need a spade and a round-nosed shovel. Sorry Ray, I know you were really looking forward to this calf."

"Ok, Dad." It wasn't really something I wanted to do or even get ready for. This wasn't supposed to have happened. Everything was ruined for this year and next for showing my calves.

School seemed to drag all day. Ms. Smith groaned her exasperation during my band lesson and seemed to be as glad it was over as I was. My saxophone was squeaking terribly, and I definitely couldn't follow the song.

I had to walk home with my little sister, Mary, after school. I couldn't carry my sax on my bike, and Mom made me walk with Mary on band lesson day to save Mom time. Mary constantly peppered me with questions and comments on the way home.

"Why did the calf die? Are you going to bury it? How deep of a hole are you going to dig? Will Ivory have another calf soon? What were you going to name the calf? I can't wait to show my bucket calf at the fair this year. My calf will be the prettiest. I have a pink halter that will match my boots and show stick. It'll be so cool."

"Mary, SHUT UP!"

She looked at me, and I'm sure it wasn't a pretty sight, then she sighed. "Ok, but you shouldn't say shut up."

We walked home in silence then, with Mary giving me a sideways glance every now and then. She would take a breath like she was going to say something, then look away. I did my homework first thing and practiced my sax, which was a complete waste of time. I went out to the shed and found the shovel and spade. Then I went to the front porch to wait for Dad.

The phone rang, and Mom answered. "Ray, it's your dad, he's running late on his calls and won't be home until after supper. Mary, help Ray set the table. Chris is helping me make supper."

"Can't Ray do it himself? I'm really doing well on Hedgehog Launch," whined Mary, her eyes glued to the old computer. "Look, Ray, I'm going for a new high score," she said as I walked by.

Mom walked in and hit the switch on the power strip. "Do what I told you, and do it now!" She gave Mary one of those I-mean-business looks.

"Ok, but you're not supposed to turn the power off like that."

Boy, was that ever a mistake. Mary wasn't going to get away with anything now. Mom just glowered at her and followed her into the kitchen. "Ray, take it easy. Mary is going to set the table by herself."

"Thanks, Mom." I needed the break.

Supper was soon ready, and Mom asked me to give the blessing. That was hard as I didn't really feel blessed, but I did it anyway. Supper was about over when I heard the door to the garage rumble open. I ran to see Dad, and he was stripping off his coveralls in the mudroom next to the kitchen. His coveralls were all bloody, and he had blood splattered all over his face and glasses. The sleeves of his shirt next to his shoulders were soaked with blood too.

"Ted Johnson's cow had a uterine prolapse, and it was a real bear to get in, which I guess is pretty obvious from the way I look. I'll get cleaned up and eat a bit. Then we can go. Do you have the shovel and spade ready?"

"Yep, they're on the porch."

"Put them in the truck, and I'll be out as soon as I finish."

Dad ate quickly and was carrying some cookies as he left the table. We were soon headed out to the pasture in the truck. Cow heads all came up as soon as they heard and saw that it was "their" truck. We got out of the truck with a little feed and filled the feed pans. The ground was shaking as they came thundering down the hill. There were only ten of them and I couldn't imagine what a huge herd of buffalo (yes, I know they are really bison!) would have sounded and felt like. We usually gave them a small amount of feed when we went out to see them so we didn't have to go looking for them. Dad said it's the lazy man's horse. The herd had black cows, a red cow, two roan cows, and of course, my White Parks. Dad said we had a mongrel herd of cows, nothing consistent about them.

Ivory stayed at the top of the hill, lowing and looking at us, then at something on the ground. We put the buckets back in the truck and picked up the shovel and spade. The cows soon finished their treat and followed us up the hill. The calves ran around the cows, kicking up their heels. We reached the top of the hill and Dad leaned on his spade, breathing a little heavily. It'd been a long day, and it wasn't over yet.

The calf was stretched out on the ground, his head swollen and the tongue sticking out. He was white with a red nose, ears, eye patches, and feet. He had red spots on his neck and shoulders. He was a red point like his grandfather. A buzzard must have started eating on him before Ivory chased it away as there was a hole under the tail. Buzzards start on the soft parts first. The flies buzzed around, and there were fly eggs all over the calf.

"Keep the calf between you and Ivory as much as you can," cautioned Dad. "She's upset with calving, let alone a dead calf, and she might do something she normally wouldn't do. A lot of cows have a change of disposition for a while after they calve."

Dad took the spade and started cutting a line in the sod and soon had a long side of a rectangle started. "Take your shovel Ray, and try to keep the sod in large pieces so we can cover the hole when we fill it back in. The calf's so stiff we'll have to make a larger hole than usual."

I started cutting under the sod, dragging large pieces to the side. The other cows came up to sniff the calf and then back off and low. It reminded me of a television show where an elephant died and the other elephants came up and touched it with their trunks. They sniffed it just like the cows were doing now. Ivory stood there, overseeing the entire process.

I finished moving the sod to the side. Then, Dad crumbled the dirt from the sides of the hole and I scooped it out. The only sounds were cows sniffing and lowing, shovels scraping, and dirt clods hitting the ground. Dad and I worked in silence, each knowing what the other person wanted them to do. I started hearing the buzzing of mosquitos as they dive-bombed my ears. I swatted at them. It was starting to get dark, and the frogs in the pond nearby boomed their nightly chorus. Sweat dripped off Dad's nose and forehead; he finally took off his glasses and put them in his pocket.

"There, let's see if it's deep enough yet." Dad measured with his spade and then stuck it in the ground, and I pulled myself out of the hole. He watched Ivory carefully as he dragged the calf over to the hole. He dropped the calf in the hole, and its feet stuck over the edge. He shook his head disgustedly and hauled the calf out.

"Nowhere close. I should've known better. I guess I wouldn't make a very good gravedigger. He won't bend since he's in rigor mortis. They say at the funeral home that sometimes they will be working on a body and as the body stiffens, it will sit up. It scares the daylights out of the person working on the body."

I snorted at the thought. Glad I didn't work there. This was bad enough. We set to work, making the hole longer and deeper. The sun was completely gone by the time we finished digging. The sky was pink and the bats flitted around our heads, making mosquitoes their supper. Dad motioned for me to get out of the hole. He grabbed the calf, folded its legs under it as well as he could, and dropped it in the hole. With a plop, it hit the bottom of the hole this time.

"That should do it. Let's fill it back in."

Ivory anxiously sniffed the edge of the hole and mooed urgently as we started throwing dirt in the hole. The other cows came and milled around, sniffing too. The calf was soon covered. The other cows lost interest, wandering off grazing. Their anxiety had eased, and they were content again. Nothing was there to remind them of death. Ivory stayed at the edge of the hole even as we covered it with sod.

"That's it, Ray. You've had a couple of late nights with nothing to show for it but a filled-in hole in the ground. That's life in the cattle business sometimes."

I just nodded, and we headed off to the truck. I dragged my shovel, and Ivory followed us, sniffing the ground where my shovel left a trail. She stopped to moo, then sniffed and followed me again. She stood there at the gate, watching as we left in the truck. She glowed in the full moon now, like a ghost. She strode back up the hill again as we drove off. I saw her grazing with the other cows until we rounded the corner and I lost sight of her.

"Ray, you know we can't afford to keep Ivory. It'll be another year before she'll have another calf, and she'll be eating all of that time. I don't want to buy another calf and put it on her because it might bring a disease into the herd, and we don't want that.

"I know, Dad. Can we talk about it tomorrow?"

"That's fine. I just wanted to say something before I forgot and too many plans were made."

Next week we loaded Ivory into Greg Jaspers's trailer. I put the halter on her and led her up and onto the trailer. I could hardly see by the time I pulled the halter off and jumped off the trailer. Greg slammed the gate behind me, and I walked away. The diesel engine rumbled, and I could hear gravel crunching as Ivory left.

Later in the week there was an envelope in the mail for me. It was a check from the sale barn. I couldn't believe how much money I had. Maybe I would buy another calf that fall. Maybe I would buy a bull, or another heifer and show her next year. There were a lot of things I could do.

Chapter 5
A Close Shave

Mom sat down at the breakfast table as I was chewing my sausage. "It's time for family pictures in a few weeks. We haven't had formal pictures taken of the family for several years and you kids are really growing up fast. Lonnie, I have already talked to Gladys and Sue so they left some time open in your clinic schedule. You can pick up Ray as soon as school gets out tomorrow. The two of you can go to the barber since you both need haircuts. Ray, you get out of school early due to teacher in-service." Dad looked at me and raised an eyebrow when he thought Mom wasn't looking. "I saw that, Lonnie. We *are* having pictures taken, and I don't want to hear any complaining or making faces about it."

"Ok, I'll pick up Ray on the north side of the school after classes are out. You'll have your sax to bring home won't you?"

"Yep," I replied. I couldn't make faces with Mom watching me.

"Mary and Chris have appointments to get their hair done next week just before the pictures next Thursday. That's the only time the photographer had open for a month. I've already scheduled that with Sue too."

The girls began to excitedly jabber about how they were going to have their hair done and what they were going to wear. Dad and I just looked at each other, knowing what we were going to have to suffer through for the next week and a half.

The next day, Dad was waiting outside the school in his truck. He was reading a veterinary magazine and talk radio was playing. I opened the door, startling him.

"Dad, why're you always reading? You don't have to take tests anymore."

"Well," he drawled like John Wayne, "I have tests every day. What would happen if there was a new treatment or information about a disease in this journal and I didn't read about it? Would an animal die or suffer just because I didn't take the time to read about it? I can't keep up on everything, so I read what I can and go to classes. I send hard cases to the specialists, or even to the vet school at Iowa State. That way, my patients get the best care."

"I get it, I've heard enough from my teachers today."

Dad smiled and started the truck. We weaved our way between cars, kids, bicycles, and buses as we left the parking lot and headed downtown. Downtown was crowded, and we had to circle around until we could find a parking place.

Dad grumbled, "We should've just parked at the clinic and walked. It would've been faster."

We walked into the barbershop, and the smell of oiled clippers and aftershave filled my nose. Deputy Peters was in the barber chair with an apron on. Richard Smith, the barber, held his hand to a machine and psssst his hand was full of warm shaving cream. He soaped up the deputy's neck and picked up a straight razor. He was putting the finishing touch on the haircut. He was a perfectionist and said clippers didn't cut the hair short enough or evenly enough on the back of your neck, around your ears, or for your sideburns. He used that shiny, wicked-looking straight razor for that. He stropped the razor by sliding it back and forth on the strap attached to the chair. He tipped the deputy's head forward and started making precise strokes down his neck, wiping the shaving cream on a towel as he worked. This was the only time I ever saw Deputy Peters quiet.

I was getting drowsy with the hum of conversation when I finally heard, "Next." It was my turn. Richard, in his white shirt and pants, was waiting by the chair with apron in hand. I had to hop a little to get into the chair. Richard pumped the handle until I was up where he could reach me, even though he wasn't very tall. He whipped the apron out and over me, and then started stuffing a stiff collar between the apron and my neck.

"How much do you want off, Ray? The usual or do you want a high and tight?"

"Just the usual. We have to have our pictures taken next week. It's the whole family, that's why Dad's here too."

"Lonnie, this boy is really growing. I don't think I'll have to pump up the chair the next time he comes in." Richard continued snipping while he talked.

"Ray, don't you show cattle at the county fair?"

"Yep, I show American British White Parks."

"My granddaughter from Alimeda is going to show pigs at the fair this year for the first time. I'd really appreciate it if you could help her out since it's her first year. Could you do that for me?"

"Sure." He has a girl for me, just like Mrs. Jones, sheesh.

"She has bright red hair so I doubt you'll miss her."

"Ok, I'll help her."

"Thanks, Ray." Then Richard went back to snipping away.

I was almost melted into in the chair while I listened to the drone of conversation around me. Bob Knox, a local insurance agent, came in and joined the conversation too. Richard started loosening the collar around my neck. I heard the hum of the shaving cream dispenser and psssst. Richard smoothed the warm shaving cream around my neck, which felt good, but I was terrified of what was next. He started stropping the razor back and forth, scrape, scrape, scrape. Then he put his hand on my head and pushed it slightly forward, resting his hand there to steady my head. I tensed up as the cold steel touched the back of my head, and he drew it down by my right ear. I knew if he slipped my ear would be sliced off. He worked around my head and to my other ear, cleaning the razor as he went, my heart beating a hundred miles an hour.

"Done."

What a wonderful word. My shoulders relaxed, and Richard started cleaning the extra shaving cream off my neck. Then he splashed on some fancy smelling stuff. I still had both of my ears, and I wasn't bleeding. What a relief. Richard pulled the apron around and dumped all of the hair into a pile to the side.

"You're next, Lonnie."

I jumped down out of the chair and went back to my *Sports Illustrated*. Dad put down his magazine and stood to stretch, stiff from sitting in the chair so long. He sat down in the chair and the conversations started again. I was soon lost in an article about the Cardinals and their new shortstop. Richard had just started shaving Dad's neck when the doorbell tinkled and Six-Pack Krebs stuck his head in the door.

He called out, "Richard, old buddy. Come and see what I just bought. I think it's an old friend of yours."

Richard stood on his tiptoes and shaded his eyes from the glare of the afternoon sun off the cars parked outside. "What've you got?"

His voice was already noticeably higher than normal. He strode to the door, razor still in hand. "My car! You bought my car I just traded in."

We all crowded up to the window and peered out. There was Richard's red Ford Taurus. He always kept it in immaculate condition, the same way he kept his shop. Suddenly a pig's head popped up over the steering wheel. It was white with a pink nose and hit the horn with its hooves. HONKKK. The pig was startled and dived back onto the floor, out of sight. Richard's face turned beet red, and he went out the door and looked in the car. Six-Pack was laughing so hard he was slapping his knees as he bobbed went up and down. Dad smiled and nodded at me to follow him out the door. Everyone else followed us.

Richard was bent over looking in the driver's side window when the pig popped up again and was nose-to-nose with Richard, only the glass between them. The pig snorted in alarm and ran to the other side. Richard's face turned purple, and the veins stood out on his neck.

He turned around, faced Six-Pack and sputtered, "You, you, you!"

Richard whirled around and started striding down the sidewalk, people scattering as he swung the razor up and down. He stepped out at a brisk pace, heading to the other end of Main Street. We all fell in behind him and kept pace. The apron was billowing out around Dad, and I trotted to keep up with him. I looked back, and Deputy Peters had a big grin on his face. The deputy was talking to Mr. Bell, the school principal. People stopped their conversations and stepped to the side as we approached.

Six-Pack followed along, guffawing and pointing out Richard to people as we passed. They asked, "You really put a pig in Richard's car?"

Six-Pack nodded, and they put their hands to their mouths to stifle laughs, then grinned and joined in the parade. They whispered to others what had happened and soon people were on cell phones talking, texting, and taking videos. Cars stopped at the sight of the parade until someone behind them gave a polite honk. Then the next car stopped to look at the parade until they were honked at.

We reached the Ford dealership, and Richard marched in. Dad caught the door before it shut and held it open as the rest of the crowd followed Richard into the dealership. Mitch Wilson, the owner, sat at his desk talking on the phone. His office had a large window so he could see the floor of the dealership out front. Richard saw him and went at full steam past the secretary. She was so surprised she didn't say anything.

Richard turned the corner, and I was right behind him in the front row. The office quickly filled as people crowded into the office. Mitch leaned back as Richard leaned over the desk, holding the razor in front of him.

Richard, his face white now, raised the razor and flicked it at Mitch for emphasis as he slowly said, "If you ever," flick, "sell that man," flick, "another car of mine," flick, "I will never," flick, "buy another car," flick, "from you again!"

Each time he flicked the razor, a bit of shaving cream, mixed with Dad's hair, flew through the air and hit Mitch. Mitch sat there in amazement, not uttering a word, shaving cream splattered all over his shirt and tie. Grins stretched from ear to ear of each onlooker. I could see Dad at the back looking through the window with the secretary. She had her hand to her mouth, stifling a laugh.

Richard turned around. "Let's get back to the shop guys. I still have to finish Lonnie's haircut."

Everyone jostled around in the tight quarters and managed to get out the door of the office. Mitch still sat there, a baffled look on his face. Dad and I followed Richard back to the shop, and he chatted about this and that like nothing had happened. The car was in front of the shop with a crowd of gawkers looking in the car. Richard ignored them and went into the shop like nothing had happened. Six-Pack was trailing along telling everyone what had happened.

We entered the deserted shop, and Richard went to the chair and motioned for Dad to get in. The razor shook in his hand as he said, "Let's finish it, Lonnie."

Dad's hand went into his pocket and pulled out his cell phone. "Hello, ok, I'll be right there. Bye, Richard, I have an emergency, I've got to get going."

He jerked the apron from his neck and handed it to Richard. He pulled out his billfold and gave Richard some money. "Keep the change. We have to get going."

Dad wiped the back of his neck with his hand as we went back out to the truck and grabbed a towel out of the back. Six-Pack was in "his" car now, the pig sitting next to him on the seat. He gave us a big wave as he backed out, honking the horn, and pointing at the pig as he did so, just for Richard's benefit.

Dad gave a chuckle and then sighed as we backed out. "That was a close one. I've never seen Richard so riled up and with good reason. I doubt Mitch ever sells another car of Richard's to Six-Pack. Six-Pack probably has home haircuts so I doubt he ever goes to a barbershop. If he does, he probably won't go here."

"Dad, what's the emergency?"

Dad smiled. "My ears wanted to stay attached to my head."

Chapter 6
Cedrick

The college students were very particular. "How much exercise will he get? Will you feed him your food or do we have to bring our own? Will you leave a night light on for him so he won't get scared? Here're his treats. He gets two each day. Here's his catnip toy. He likes to play with it most of the day. The scratching post doesn't look like it will fit in the cage."

Cedrick peered out from behind all of his toys, his rear end wiggling. He jumped to the front of the cat condo and attacked my fingers. He growled and rolled around on his back.

"We only have part of a semester of college left and the apartment manager said we couldn't keep Cedrick or he would evict us. That nasty neighbor turned us in when he heard Cedric meowing while we were in class. We couldn't give Cedrick away; he's just such a darling," cooed Shari Shannon.

"We found him under our car in the rain, and he looked so pathetic we just had to keep him."

Sue had listened to them talk for over half an hour, putting up with their questions and their directions about how to take care of their little Cedrick. Her eyes were starting to glaze over when they finally decided everything was ok. They fussed all the way back to the front desk as they were leaving.

Sue went to the computer. "Your deposit will be $165. We can take cash, check, debit card, or credit card. You can pay the rest when you pick him up."

The two of them looked at each other, and Shari started digging through her bag. "I guess we left our debit card at home and our credit card is maxed out. It's a good thing you said something, since we have to get groceries. I'll have to go home and get it so we have something to eat tonight. We'll be back in a few days to check on Cedrick."

"Here's a twenty for the deposit. We'll be back," said her husband, Bob, and he turned and walked out the door.

Sue called out, "We'll need the rest of the deposit then."

Sue turned and looked at me as the door shut. "They didn't have any intention of paying today. I'll bet you they don't pay again next time either. There's a reason they drove twenty-five miles to board their cat."

I went back to look at Cedrick and play with him. Cedrick came to the front of the cage, purring and rubbing his face on the door. His silver tabby coat glowed as he paced back and forth in the cage. I started rubbing his head through the door, and the purring really revved up. I heard another animal moving in the cage next to him and looked at it. Suddenly claws were attached to my finger, trying to pull it into Cedrick's cage. Cedrick had decided to play, and my finger was a great toy.

"Ouch!" I pulled my finger out and looked at the jagged scratch marks that were starting to ooze blood.

Cedrick looked at me, devilry in his eyes, and then he jumped forward and grabbed my shirt sleeve, snagging it with his claws. I jumped back but a thread stuck to one claw, leaving a hole in my shirt. He lay on his side then with his front legs hanging out of the front of the cage. He stretched out his legs toward me, his claws unsheathed, grabbing for me. He gave up after a minute of that and looked at me, daring me to do something.

I looked through his box of toys and found a fishing pole with a catnip filled fish on a string. I waved it back and forth about a foot in front of his cage. He was instantly up, crouched in attack mode, his eyes intently fixed on the fish, his tail swishing back and forth. I started jerking the fish up and down, banging it against the cage and pulling it away. He started wiggling his rear end.

POW. He jumped and hit the front of the cage, hitting his head and grabbing the fish. He dragged the fish into the cage, growling and biting. He held it against his chest and started digging at it with his rear feet. Each day after that, I played with Cedrick until he was exhausted or I had to do chores. Usually I had to do chores.

Shari Shannon came back the next week to see Cedrick. "My, how you have grown," gushed Shari. "Here are some more treats and toys for him. We found a new apartment and will be moving next week. We'll pick him up as soon as we are settled. See you then," she said and breezed out the door.

Sue stared open-mouthed. "She didn't even give me a chance to ask her for the rest of the deposit. She'll forget to pay next time too. Mark my words, that woman has no intention of paying anything more. She can buy treats and toys but can't pay us."

That following weekend Dad and I went down to clean kennels on Saturday night as Edie, the kennel supervisor, was gone for the weekend. "Dad, can we let Cedrick out of his condo for the weekend?"

Dad nodded. "Go ahead, just make sure the door is open and he knows where his litter box is."

I opened Cedrick's cage door, and he bounced out and started running around the room. I pulled his fish along the floor and ran around the room with him in pursuit. I swung the fish in circles faster and faster, making him dizzy. I flipped it at him and to see how high he could jump. Finally I took off through the clinic with him hot on my heels after the fish.

"Ray, we need to finish cleaning the kennels. You walk the dogs while I clean the kennels. Put Cedrick back in his condo and shut the door first. One of the dogs might do him some damage. We're going out for supper tonight since it's the first free night we have all had as a family in a while."

"Ok Dad." I gathered up Cedrick and put him back in the condo, shutting the cage door before he could worm his way out.

I pulled out the hose for Dad, and I grabbed a leash from the rack. Most of them had to really go, and would do their business right away, so Dad had to hurry. Many of them boarded at the clinic a lot and knew what the routine was. They wanted to eat, so I didn't have to walk them far. Buford was the exception; he's a sixty pound beagle that should weigh twenty-five pounds at most. His back was flat because of all the fat, and he was shaped like a coffee table because his fat stuck out over the edges around him. He waddled outside with me, baying at everything he saw just to prove he was still a hunting dog, able to chase a rabbit all day if only in his imagination.

He stopped and lifted his leg to do his business on everything he saw, even the flowers Mom had planted. I couldn't drag him away, and he stayed there no matter how much I tugged on the leash and yelled at him. He just stared at me with soulful eyes until he decided he was done. I knew the flowers would turn brown wherever the urine hit them, and Mom wouldn't be happy. Hopefully she would think the clients brought their dogs around here and let them go on her flowers. He had lifted his leg for what seemed like the twentieth time when it started to spit rain. The rain didn't faze Buford one bit as he wandered around in search of the perfect place to do his number two job.

He was sniffing around next to the vacant lot when he hit a hot rabbit trail. "Aoooooohhhh-hhhh." He was off! The leash yanked my arm, and my head snapped back. I started running just so I wouldn't fall down. The tall weeds whipped my face, and I was soon soaking wet. Buford was in full voice, as the hunters say, and dragging me. I couldn't set my feet to pull back and stop him. My arms were scratched, and I couldn't let go of the leash since it was around my wrist. He might have chased the rabbit all night if I had let go anyway. I saw the rabbit dodge around an old pile of lumber that had been thrown over the fence from the lumberyard. I hit a board that was sticking out and went face first into the ground. Buford hit the end of the leash, gave a yip, and flipped around, about jerking my arm out of its socket. He kept jumping and pulling on the leash, yelling for that rabbit, but he couldn't budge me now.

I spit some dirt out of my mouth and yelled, "Buford! Buford!" He turned and looked at me, so I rolled over and sat up. "Buford, sit!"

Buford sat down, panting heavily with his tongue hanging out, and I got up. I was covered with stick tights and beggar's lice. My jeans were muddy from rolling around on the ground, and the rain was still coming down. Buford sat there with his tongue lolling, whimpering, still eager to get the rabbit. That was a lot of work for an overweight beagle. He had done his job to his satisfaction and wanted to keep looking for another rabbit.

"Come on Buford. Let's get inside before Dad wonders what happened to us."

Buford obediently followed me now, still eager for the chase, but the excitement had worn off enough he would listen. There was no way he could ever catch a rabbit. Besides, beagles are just supposed to chase rabbits, not catch them. It was raining hard now as we headed back to the clinic. I was suddenly jerked to a stop, and my feet went out from under me on the mud. Splash! I landed in a puddle. Buford stared me in the face. He was squatting and doing the business he had forgotten to do earlier. I stood up, my cold, wet pants sticking to my legs, and watched Buford as he finished. He started strutting and scratching the ground to mark his turf, scattering rocks all over. Great, now I would have to bring a shovel out and clean up the mess since it was in the parking lot and not the grass.

The bell dinged as we went back into the clinic and Dad yelled, "What took you so long?"

Buford started pulling me back to the kennels, now in anticipation of supper. He had worked up an appetite, as if he didn't ever have one. I let the leash slip off my wrist as we came to the door, and he ran into the kennel and started wolfing down his supper. I followed him into the kennel room.

Dad took one look at me and started laughing. "We sure have glamorous jobs, don't we? We'll get you home and cleaned up before we go to eat. You can tell everyone what happened to you while we're eating. I have the rest of the chores done."

"I have to take a shovel out front and clean up Buford's mess first, Dad."

"I'll get some towels to sit on so you don't make a big mess in my truck. I have Cedrick set for the rest of the weekend. He has the whole clinic to roam around now."

Cedrick had the run of the place after that. He would tease the dogs in their runs after he learned they couldn't reach them. He would sidle up to a run and reach in and bat at a dog until they turned around after him. He was king of the clinic in just a few days.

The day came when Cedrick was scheduled to go home. I said my goodbyes the night before since I would be in school when he went home. I was on my way home from school when Dad was driving by and spotted me. "Do you want a ride to the clinic?"

"Sure," I said and scrambled into the passenger seat.

"Ray, most of the animals went home Monday, so there aren't many chores to do. I don't have anything else scheduled for the afternoon. We'll go to baseball practice after you are finished so you can get in a little extra batting practice."

We pulled into the garage and went inside. Something immediately attacked my shoelaces.

"Cedrick, you're still here!"

"What did I tell you Ray? They aren't going to pay. They're just going to dump him on us," said Sue, her face red. "I knew we couldn't trust those people."

I was secretly happy but didn't say so. I knew Dad needed the money for the clinic, but I was happy anyway. I did all of my chores, and we left for baseball practice. Cedrick was still there, checking out his kingdom.

The next day I walked into the clinic and, sure enough, Cedrick was still there. He pounced on me as soon as I walked through the door. I grabbed his fish and led him on a chase through the clinic.

I went up front. Sue had a knowing look on her face. "I called the owners, and their phone has been disconnected. I called the emergency number they left for an aunt, and all she would say was, 'I wondered what happened to that cat.' I called the manager of the apartment complex, and he said they moved out in the middle of the night last weekend. They were behind in their rent and left a big mess."

"Does that mean he gets to stay?"

"You'll have to ask your dad about that."

I went running to Dad's office in the back of the clinic. "Sue said that the people that brought Cedrick in are gone. Can we keep him?"

"Ray, first of all, he still belongs to those people. We have to give them a chance to pick him up and pay their bill. I doubt they will, since they moved, but we have to follow the law. They have seven days to redeem him, and we have to send a notice to them. Secondly, we can't have a cat at home since your mother is allergic. Third, we really don't need a cat here at the clinic."

"Ok, but could we possibly keep him here at the clinic?"

"I'll think about it and see what Sue and Gladys think too."

Each day I went to the clinic and Cedric was there to greet me as soon as I stepped through the door. He even started retrieving syringe cases when I threw them, bouncing off a door and into another room. His feet slid out from under him as he cornered. He came running back and dropped the case on the counter next to me. I knew Gladys liked him, and I thought Sue was thawing a bit. He would run up to the front of the clinic when he heard the bell, jump on the counter, and greet clients when they walked in the door. Some of the farmers wrestled with him, and if he heard Matt Schrage's voice, he sprinted to the front, ready for a tussle.

One day Sue had a self-satisfied look on her face. "Yesterday was the date Cedrick's owners had to reply by. The letter came back since they didn't leave a forwarding address with the post office. I told you they weren't going to pay. Now your dad can do whatever he wants with him. All new clients are supposed to pay ahead of time or leave a credit card number with a release so we can bill them, but they were sneaky. I'm sure they've done that type of thing before since they skipped out on their apartment rent too."

Blah, blah, blah, all I could think was that Cedrick would be mine if Dad would let me keep him. I hurried and did my chores. Dad came in carrying his ultrasound, so I ran out to his truck and brought in more of his stuff.

Dad looked beat, but I couldn't wait. "Dad, Sue said the time was up for Cedrick's owners to claim him. Can we keep him?"

Dad gave one of his sighs. "We do need a blood donor sometimes. We'll have to test him for several diseases, and they will have to be negative before we can keep him. Go tell Gladys that we are going to test him and that she can set up the tests."

I sprinted up and told Gladys what we were going to do. She smiled and gave me a conspiratorial wink. "Go get Cedrick. I'll meet you in the treatment area."

Cedrick thought it was play time and ran away every time I tried to pick him up. I finally pulled the fish around and threw it in a cage. Cedrick dashed into the cage, and I slammed the door shut. This time he knew the jig was up, so he let me pick him up and carry him to the treatment area. Gladys had a towel, syringe, bandage, cotton, and alcohol ready.

"Dr. Morrison, will you help us draw blood since Sue is helping someone up front?"

Dad came over while Gladys expertly wrapped Cedrick in a towel. Cedrick, king of the clinic, did not take well to the indignity of being restrained. He yowled while Dad drew blood out of his back leg. Gladys set up the tests, and I anxiously waited to see how many blue spots would show up in the little window.

"A watched pot never boils, Ray. Take a break and it will seem to go faster," said Gladys. "I'll let you know if there is a problem."

I started looking at the insert and found the part in English, but decided to practice my Spanish and started reading that section. I found where the control spot was supposed to show up, that is the only one I wanted to turn blue. A spot anywhere else might mean that I couldn't keep Cedrick.

"Ray," Gladys waved me over. "You can look at it now."

There was one small blue spot in the window. "Does that mean he's negative? Do we get to keep him?"

Gladys laughed. "These tests are negative, but we have more to send in to the lab. We need to vaccinate him and give him boosters, as he is due for vaccinations. Go get him. It's up to your dad as to whether we keep him, but I hope we do."

The next two days seemed to take forever as we waited for the results. I came down to the clinic after school and on the back counter was a fax from the laboratory with Cedrick's results. Everything looked ok to me, but I didn't understand the blood type thing. I took the fax and went looking for Dad. He was in an exam room with a client so I knew better than to bother him until he was done. I sat in a chair, cooling my heels as Dad would say, but I was tapping my foot. I had too much energy to sit still.

Dad finished with the client, and I just held up the fax. He came over and pretended to read it. I could see his eyes were not focusing on it. He had already looked at it. I knew I had to let him keep me in suspense a while longer or he wouldn't ever tell me.

Finally, he looked over the top of the paper. "Everything looks good, but I don't think he will make a good blood donor the way he fought us drawing blood. We'll keep him though. Congratulations, you have a cat."

"Yes." I jumped up. "Thanks Dad. Cedrick can stay as King of the Clinic."

Chapter 7
Rafter Jump

Dad pulled the truck through the fancy, black, wrought iron gates to the horse barn. A little, dried-up old man with an unlit cigar in his mouth was sitting on a bale of straw under the lean to. He stood up and walked over to the truck like a gunslinger, his bowed legs swinging side to side.

Dad opened the door, and the little man took the cigar out of his mouth and spat. "Doc, the colt must be backwards because the soles of the feet are facing up. She hasn't been at it too long, so the colt should be ok."

"We'll check it out," said Dad as he walked around to the back of the truck and opened up his vet box. "Is Dave around tonight, or is he gone on a business trip?"

"The boss and his wife are gone on another trip. I knew something would happen since he's gone. This's his St. Pat mare. 'Member, she was the orphan born on St Patrick's Day that I raised several years ago?"

Dad was filling his bucket with warm water and disinfectant, and I could see his eyebrows rise a little in the weak light from the barn. "Do you have her tied up?"

"She's fine, Doc. I have 'er tied to the manger in the old box stall."

Dad gathered his bucket, OB sleeves, and lube, and we went to the barn. I looked at the fancy show wagon with all of the shiny brass on it parked in the corner. Harness was hanging in the tack room with horse collars with brass on them also. Dad and Stan went into the stall, and I peered around the corner. A big, black Percheron mare stood in the stall, grunting as she strained, raising her tail and hunching her back trying to push the foal out. Two black hooves stuck out of the back of her, the soft white soles pointing at the sky.

"Ray, you stay out of the stall in case she swings around or goes down." Dad started wrapping the short tail to keep it out of the way and keep things clean. He pulled out his OB sleeves and put on some lube to make things slick. He reached in and started feeling around. The mare grunted. "Ouch, she sure can push. I feel ears instead of a tail. The foal is coming upside down with his head pointed toward his chest. Let me see if I can straighten out his head."

Dad tugged and pushed, straining for all he

was worth as the mare did the same. He worked a little, then got some more lube and went back to it. He even had both arms inside at the same time, pushing with one and pulling with the other. It seemed like he was never going to get the foal, when suddenly he about fell over backwards.

"The head came forward, now I just have to get it right side up. I'm going to try twisting the legs. Ready, here it goes."

Dad held onto each leg. He twisted them clockwise, and the mare gave a big grunt. Half of the colt came out, and then she gave another big grunt. The colt popped onto the ground as Dad jumped out of the way. It rolled over and sat up, staring up at Dad with wide open, surprised eyes.

"Wow, that was one fast delivery as soon as he was straightened out. Stan, let's pull the foal up to the front of St. Pat so she can see it and mother it. I'll give her an antibiotic shot and tetanus antitoxin just to be safe since I had my arms in her so many times."

Stan came around with Dad, and they each grabbed a leg to pull the foal up to the front of the mare. The mare let out a squeal and swung around, kicking. Stan went down on top of the colt, and Dad jumped into the manger. The mare calmed down then and quit kicking.

Stan, pulled himself up to his knees, picked up his old, rolled up, felt cowboy hat and stood up. His creased, brown face broke into a grin. "That was a close one, Doc. I guess she don't like you, she just don't like no one but me. These here orphans are a different critter, that's for sure. I'll pull the little troublemaker out of the way, then you can get your stuff."

Stan started tugging on the colt. The colt was as big as him and trying to get up. Stan gave a heave and let go of the colt, then reached down and grabbed for a moving leg and gave another heave, pulling the colt a few inches. Sweat dripped off the tip of his nose as he gave a final heave and the colt was safely out of the way on the other side of St. Pat. He stood up with his hand on his back. "I'll need to go to the chiropractor after that. I think she put something out of place when she knocked me down."

Dad started to get out of the manger, and the mare squealed again, letting both of her back hooves fly. They hit the wall next to Dad, so he jumped back into the manger. St Pat kept squealing and kicking, her hooves hitting the wall next to Dad. A few kicks later, Dad moved in the manger away from the flying hooves toward the front of her. She swung her head around toward him, her teeth clicking together a foot from his face. She kept trying to bite him, so Dad was stuck between flying hooves and a wicked bite and being shook like a rat. Dad suddenly climbed the wall behind the manger.

The mare kept an eye on him as he worked his

way along the top of the stall. He inched his way to the corner and stretched until he had navigated the turn. He came to the door of the stall and a shower of dirt and dust came down on me.

"Move, Ray. I'm going to jump down." Dad sat with his legs in the door, then turned around and his feet hung there. He gave a little push back and swung with his arms like a gymnast, landing outside the stall. He hit the dirt and rolled over onto his back. When he stood up there was a line of dust running down his coveralls and shirt. His face was red and his hands trembled.

"I don't think I would get a good score for that landing, but for me, it was perfect. I'm out of the stall and didn't get hurt. That was a close one. She would have killed me if she had gotten me into a corner or bit me. If she bit me, she would have tossed me around like a rag doll and then stomped me to death. I'm glad we're in this old barn and there's an old fashioned manger for me to get into." I just nodded my head at everything he said.

We went over to the door of the stall. St. Pat still kept her eye on us. The foal was already standing, taking unsteady steps as it looked for its first drink of milk. Stan was talking soothingly into the mare's ear.

"Stan, would you please get my stuff and bring it out here?"

Stan shuffled over and pick up Dad's bucket and

everything that had spilled out of it. He was bent over as he came to the door.

"How bad are you hurt?"

"I've been worse. The chiro will jump up and down on me and get me back into shape." He smiled.

"Is there any way we can get a shot into St. Pat?" asked Dad.

"I could put a Scotch hobble on 'er and a twitch. I don't think a twitch would be enough by itself."

"Do you think you can hold her with your back out?"

"Ah, she'll listen to me now, and I won't give 'er any choice as to what she does. I'll go get the ropes and twitch."

Stan moved slowly down the barn and into the tack room. Dad went out to the truck. Stan came back with two cotton ropes and a twitch made out of an axe handle with a piece of rope run through it. He walked up to the mare and tied a bowline knot with the rope around St. Pat's neck—a bowline knot wouldn't slip and get tighter so the rope wouldn't pull the noose and strangle her. He tied the longer rope to it, then ran it down around her back leg on that side and then back up to the rope on her neck. He pulled until her back leg was pulled forward and she was standing on three legs. Dad came back in with a couple of syringes and with an alcohol soaked piece of cotton.

"I'll put the twitch on, and then you should be able to get the shots into 'er, Doc."

He put his hand through the loop of rope on the axe handle, gripped St. Pat's upper lip, and slipped the loop over the lip. He then started twisting the rope until it was tight on her lip.

"Ok, Doc. I think it should be safe for you now."

St. Pat glared at Dad as he made a wide berth around her back legs and dodged the foal as it tried to nurse her. Her wide open eye stared at him as he wiped down her neck with the cotton. He pinched a spot on her neck and pushed on it with his finger as he quickly stuck the needle in. He pulled on the plunger to see if it was in a blood vessel and when no blood came, gave the injection. He did the same thing with the other syringe and then beat a hasty retreat out of the stall.

Stan was still talking to St. Pat as he took off the twitch and then the Scotch hobble. He stood back and watched as the foal finally latched onto a teat and noisily sucked away. St. Pat relaxed and nickered to the colt. She licked the parts of the colt she could reach.

"I'll shut the stall door if you want to let her go, Stan?"

"She's ok now, Doc. Go ahead and shut the door."

Dad slid the door shut, and Stan took the lead rope off of St. Pat. I peered through the bars in the upper part of the stall when St. Pat came over to the door and struck like a snake at a gap between the bars of the stall. Dad and I both jumped back, stumbling to stay up.

Stan came up to St. Pat. "You daft horse," he yelled and waved his hat at her. "Don't ya know he just saved your life and your little one too?"

She backed off then and went over to her colt, who was still trying to nurse for all it was worth. Stan slid the door open enough to slide through and then shut it.

"Thanks, Doc. I'm sure Dave'll be happy when he hears she had a live foal. She's just plain dangerous to anyone but me. I hope she doesn't have anything else go wrong with her. I'll be prepared next time though if you have to do something to 'er."

"I was a little busy so I didn't look. Is it a stud colt or a filly?"

"It's a filly, Doc, a nice black filly like 'er mother."

I helped carry everything out to the truck. Stan followed along, shuffling even more than when we had arrived. I climbed into the truck. Stan waved, turned, and went back into the barn as we pulled out of the lot.

Every time we drove by the farm, I kept an eye out for the little filly and her mother, St. Pat, the horse that wanted to kill my dad even though he was helping her.

Chapter 8
Can You See?

Mary came bounding up as Dad and I walked in the door. "Dad, I have a note for you from Ms. Rodriguez." Mary held up a piece of paper. "We're talking about community helpers and she wants you to talk to the class about your job. Will you do it please? I told her you would bring Cy along." Mary looked up at Dad with puppy dog eyes.

Dad opened the note and read through it. "Ok, I'll have to check my schedule and give Ms. Rodriguez a call. What's for supper, Mary?"

The next night at supper Dad said, "Mary, I talked to Ms. Rodriguez today, and I'm going to talk to your class next Thursday."

"Goody," squealed Mary. "You're going to bring Cy, aren't you? I told everyone that you would bring him."

"Yes, I'm going to bring Cy and different instruments to show the class. Ray, I asked her if you could help me carry things to the class since I'm going to have Cy, and she said it was ok. I guess you'll get out of class for a while anyway." Then he smiled and nodded at me when Mom couldn't see.

Thursday finally arrived and over the intercom came Ms. Wenger's nasal voice, "Ray Morrison, come to the office." Mr. Clark nodded at me, and I gathered my books and went out to my locker. Dad was waiting in the office, and we went out to the truck. Cy had his nose smooshed against the passenger side window of the truck, leaving streaks all over. Dad opened the door, and Cy jumped down and greeted me. Dad put his leash on him and had me hold him while he pulled a few boxes out of the truck.

"Here, Ray, you take this bigger box of things." He handed me the box, took back the leash, and picked up the small box and his long white pole syringe. Dad already had his visitor's pass, so we went straight to Mary's classroom. Dad knocked on the door, and Ms. Rodriguez came to the door and let us in.

Whispering instantly started as soon as Cy walked into the room. "Nice doggy, come here doggy." Cy stayed at heel and started panting while he sat down and looked around the room. Dad handed the leash to me so I could watch him while Dad talked.

Ms. Rodriguez cleared her throat. "Class, this is Mary's father, Dr. Morrison. He's a veterinarian and is going to talk about his job." She squinted and tilted her head. "Let's be quiet and respectful while he talks, then you can ask questions. Please hold up your hand if you have a question and wait until you are called on before you ask your question. Dr. Morrison, go ahead."

"How many of you have pets?" About half of the class raised their hands. "How many of you have a horse or a cow or a lamb?" Two kids raised their hands. "How many of you have taken your animal to a veterinarian? I recognize several of you." A quarter of the class raised their hands.

One little girl started talking, "My dog was really sick and we took him to the vet and he died."

Dad paused, and Ms. Rodriguez glared at the little girl. "Missy, you're not to talk unless you are called on. Go ahead, Dr. Morrison."

"How many of you have eaten a hamburger?" The entire class raised their hands. "Did you know that veterinarians inspect food to make sure it's safe to eat?"

The kids shook their heads.

"Veterinarians also do research. They design vaccines, antibiotics, prosthetic or fake joints, and a lot of other things. I have a classmate that works on fish. Veterinarians work in zoos, and there is even a small zoo where I work on the animals also. Veterinarians work for the government, including NASA and other organizations. A veterinarian was working in Houston when they landed on the moon and he had to say if it was ok for them to get outside of the space capsule and walk on the moon. Did you know that many veterinarians are in the armed forces? Several of my classmates are in the Air Force, the Army, and the Navy. They take care of the animals and also do many public health services to make sure disease doesn't spread in animals or people. We don't want our people in the service to get sick, and we have to keep their animals healthy also."

Hands shot up into the air. Ms. Rodriguez pointed to a boy in the front row. "Yes, Alejandro, what do you want to ask Dr. Morrison?"

"Have you ever worked on a guard dog?"

"I treat several different dogs the police have for their work. I wasn't in the service, so I haven't worked on any of their dogs."

"Did they try to bite you?"

"The police are very careful and train their dogs to behave. I've never had a problem, but like any animal, they can be scared and bite. I've had other dogs bite me, usually when I'm not careful and don't pay attention to what they are trying to tell me."

Dad grabbed his long white pole syringe and held it out in front of him. "This is what I use to give animals an injection when I can't get close enough to give them an injection."

Dad jabbed it in Alejandro's direction, and Alejandro jumped. "See how far away I can reach?

I don't have a needle on it, or I wouldn't point it toward you. A dog will often bite at it, so I have to have someone distract him so I can give him an injection. I can reach across a fence and give a cow an injection too."

Cy stood up and started looking around and whining. Dad was still talking about the pole syringe and how he used it. Cy started walking in a small circle.

"Dad, Cy has to poop!"

The room erupted: "Gross." "Oh, I think I'm going to throw up."

Dad whirled around. "Ray, hurry up and take him outside. Don't let him stop!"

I gave a tug on the leash and headed for the door. I ran down the hallway with Cy loping next to me, his toenails clicking on the hard floor. We went around the corner, and Cy slid sideways, caught himself, and away we went again. Mrs. Thompson stepped out of the office, and Cy ran into the open door, knocking papers all over.

"Ray, don't run. Help me pick up these papers."

"I can't. He has to go to the bathroom. If I stop, he'll go right here."

"Keep moving then."

I slowed down for the door outside, and Cy started to squat as he walked. I pulled him through the door and soon as he was outside, he started squatting again as he walked. I finally worked him over to the grass at the side of the door, and he walked in a circle as he squatted. He finally stopped circling and did his job right outside the office. He finished and started strutting and scratching, marking his turf, proud of the job he had done.

It was a nice spring day, and the office window was open. I could hear the people in the office talking while Cy did his duty. Suddenly I heard, "Whew, what stinks?" Then someone else, "Wow, that really smells."

I could see a figure moving toward the window, so I gave Cy a quick tug and headed back for the door before they could see who I was. I heard the window squeaking as they cranked it shut.

Cy's nails clicked on the floor as he trotted along, his head held high, not a care in the world, happy with what he had accomplished. Mrs. Thompson was gone, and I hoped I wasn't in trouble. I peered through the window of the classroom door. A little girl saw me and started pointing and whispering. Dad was holding up an X-Ray for everyone to see the broken leg he had fixed with a pin. The whispering and pointing made him turn around, then he motioned for me to come in.

I came in and heard the word "Poop" followed by a lot of giggling.

"Class, remember what we said about being quiet for our guests," Ms. Rodriguez admonished them.

Dad pulled out a pistol grip syringe next. "This

is what we use to give vaccinations to a large group of animals. We put a needle on it and can adjust the dosage so each animal gets the same amount. We can also give antibiotics or other medicine, like vitamins, this way too." He pulled out a long spinal needle next. "This is what we use to give epidurals so an animal is numb and we can operate on them and they can't feel anything."

I looked away from the needle and saw a little girl fall out of her chair and hit the floor with a resounding thump. Ms. Rodriguez went running over to her and knelt down beside her. "Alejandro, go get the school nurse. Tell her Brianna has fainted."

Alejandro went running out the door and the whole class gathered in a circle around Brianna. Ms. Rodriguez looked up. "Class, go to your seats. Brianna will be ok."

Ms. Rodriguez cradled Brianna's head in her lap. Suddenly Cy leaned over and licked Brianna on the face. The whole class piped up, "Oh gross." "Yuck." "He licked her."

I pulled him away, and Brianna started moving. Nurse Carlson came rushing in the door and knelt down to look at Brianna. She took her pulse and looked her over. "I see you have a bit of a bump on your head, Brianna. Are you feeling ok now?"

"Yes, what happened? I saw the long needle, and then I felt something wet on my cheek."

Nurse Carlson looked around. "What happened?"

"Dad held up a needle, and she fainted. She fell down on the floor, and then Cy licked her," I said.

Nurse Carlson smiled. "I guess a dog lick will revive a person. Brianna, I will take you down to my office. We'll put an ice pack on your bump. You should be ok soon and ready to come back to class."

"Can I pet the dog before I go?"

Nurse Carlson looked at me, and I nodded yes. Nurse Carlson helped Brianna up and she came over. "Nice doggy, nice doggy," she said and petted him on the head. Cy panted and tried to lick her again, but this time I was ready and held him back.

"I think we better go to my office now." Nurse Carlson gently guided Brianna to the door.

Ms. Rodriguez looked at Dad. "Do you have anything else for the class? I don't know if we can top the last one for excitement."

"I would like to show them a few things with Cy. Bring him over to the corner here where there is some extra room. Class, gather around in a circle so you can see what I am doing."

Dad picked up his box and carried it over to the corner. I held Cy while Dad rummaged around in his box. Dad pulled out a toothbrush and toothpaste with a flourish. "How many of you brush your dog or cat's teeth?"

Everyone in the room shook their heads.

"Ok, I'll show you how easy it can be. Cy's very good at letting me do this. Not all animals will let you do this, so be careful that you aren't bitten. Let your parents try it first."

Dad rolled up Cy's lip. "See how nice his teeth are? His toothpaste is poultry flavored. Dogs and cats don't like toothpaste that foams up like ours." He applied a little toothpaste to the brush. "Now see how I brush, just like you would brush your own teeth."

Cy started licking the toothpaste. Now there were more comments: "He likes it." "What does that taste like?" "I think my dog would bite me." There was also the usual: "Gross."

Dad rummaged around in his box again. He pulled out a jar with a heart in it and held it up with a flourish. "What's that?" "Oh." "It's dead." "I think I'm going to puke."

Dad began, "This is a heart from a dog that died from heartworms. If you look carefully you can see the worms sticking out of the blood vessels of the heart. They're white and long."

The kids crowded around to look at the heart. Mary was telling everyone what to do and when to move on. The kids started moving over to Cy and petting him. He was loving it. Suddenly one of the kids pulled Cy's collar over his head and off he went with some of the kids running after him and others running away screaming. Dad just shook his head and looked at me. I started calling Cy, but he was having so much fun he wouldn't come. He would disappear under a group of kids that were hugging and petting him, then suddenly wiggle free and head for another corner of the room, especially if there was a kid crying because they were scared of a 110 pound Labrador. He just wanted to see what the commotion was about, and he loved everyone. Ms. Rodriguez tried to get the class calmed down but to no effect.

I started chasing him then and yelled at the top of my lungs, "CY SIT!" The whole room silenced, and Cy plopped his rear end on the ground. He just sat there looking at me, his tongue lolling out of the side of his mouth, with saliva dripping all over the floor. I walked up to him and slipped his leash and collar over his head.

Ms. Rodriguez cleared her throat. "Thank you, Raymond. Class, lets thank Dr. Morrison, Raymond, and Cy for giving such an interesting talk about community helpers."

The class clapped and said, "Thank you."

Dad just gathered up his things and said, "You're welcome. Let's go, Ray."

We headed for the door, and Dad stopped at the office and dropped off his visitor's pass. We went to the truck and loaded his equipment. Cy jumped into the truck, sitting in his usual spot.

"Now I know why they say you should never work in entertainment with kids or animals. They'll always show you up. I'll see you at supper tonight."

That night at supper Mary was telling everyone

else in the family about what had happened in her class with Dad that morning. She was giggling when she talked about Cy having to poop and what all of the kids did. She then talked about Brianna fainting and Nurse Carlson coming to the class. Brianna came back to class for lunch and was fine other than a bump on the head.

Mary turned to me. "Ray, Mrs. Thompson wanted to know who the blind guy was you were helping."

"Blind guy? What blind guy is she talking about?"

"The one with the big yellow dog and the long white cane." Mary burst out laughing.

Dad turned red, and then I started laughing too. Mom started cracking up too, and then Chris caught on and started laughing.

"I just can't get any respect," said Dad, and he went back to eating.

Chapter 9
Mother's Day

"Let us pray." Pastor McAdams had just finished his sermon. I saw something stir in the doorway at the back of the sanctuary as I bowed my head.

"Amen. Let us sing Psalm 118 C and remain standing for the benediction."

I glanced back and saw Bob Howell standing in the doorway in his chore clothes. I nudged Dad and nodded my head toward the door. Dad gave me a puzzled look, then glanced over his shoulder. He saw Bob and sighed. The precentor started the singing, and Dad stepped around me and went back to talk to Bob.

The singing stopped, and Pastor McAdams pronounced the benediction. As we sang the last psalm verse, Dad came back.

He leaned over me toward Mom and whispered, "Dear, let's go. Bob Howell has a cow I need to look at right away."

Mom gathered her Bible, purse, and papers and quickly said her goodbyes. We went to the door of the sanctuary where Pastor McAdams was greeting and talking to people as they left. Bob Howell was nowhere to be seen. We hurriedly said hello and goodbye to Pastor McAdams and rushed out past everyone.

"Another emergency?" called out Dick Wilson as we went by.

"It'll be a messy business," replied Dad.

We piled into the van, and Mom turned and asked, "Lonnie, what's the big emergency that couldn't even wait until we made it home?"

"He has a cow with a prolapsed uterus. He has a lot of company coming over for Mother's Day and wanted to make sure we could get there as quickly as possible."

Mom sniffed. "So much for my Mother's Day dinner. Your parents are coming over in just a little bit. I know your mother will be disappointed." She sniffed again as a tear rolled down her cheek.

"I know, but the good thing is that the earlier I get to it, the easier it'll be, and the faster I can fix it and get home. The longer it sits the more it swells and the harder it is to get it back into place. I should be able to get home in time for dinner if it goes well. It'll also be better for the cow."

The frustration came out in Mom's voice. "It would just be nice to have a relaxing day without worrying about whether you will be there or not.

It seems like something comes up every time we have plans."

Dad patted her arm. "I appreciate your patience with all that you put up with."

Mom sniffed again and faced forward. Dad started the van, and we headed home. Everyone else was still in church, talking and catching up on the past week. Mother's Day dinners would have to wait for a while.

We were ready to pull into the garage when Dad asked me, "Ray, would you go along and help? You can carry things so I can get done faster."

"Sure, Dad."

Mom nodded at me with a slight smile. Dad and I hustled out of the van and changed clothes. I could hear the garage door opening, and Dad was getting things ready when I came back into the garage. He had his big Buhner needle in a bucket with water and disinfectant.

"Hop in, Ray. I'm just getting my lidocaine ready for the epidural."

I was pulling on my seatbelt when Dad sat behind the steering wheel. We roared out of the driveway and didn't slow down until we were turning onto Bob Howell's road. Dust billowed behind the truck, and we slid sideways on the gravel around one turn.

"There's Bob's place, the one with the blue silos." Dad pointed as we turned into a long lane. Cars were parked on both sides of the lane. "How many people are here? He didn't say anything about such a big crowd."

People were standing outside the house, talking as we pulled around near the barn. Bob left a group of people and came over to the barn. The group started following him and then more and more people came out of the house. Dad stepped out of the truck as Bob walked up.

"Doc, most of the family have never seen a prolapsed uterus or seen it put back in. Hope you don't mind an audience?"

Dad shook his head. "The more the merrier." He didn't say it with much enthusiasm though.

Dad started getting out his bucket. "Bob, do you have her in the chute?"

"Doc, the chute is broken, so I have her in a small pen. She's tame, and it shouldn't be any kind of problem to rope her."

Dad turned and looked at me, his face stony. "Ray, carry the bucket, I'll get the rope and halter. Here, carry this tote with the lidocaine and sleeves."

"Bob, where is she?"

"Right this way, Doc." Bob turned and headed for the old ramshackle barn.

Dad followed Bob, and I was behind him. I could hear all kinds of people talking. Thirty people followed us to the barn. Some of them were dressed up and others had on cut-offs showing tattoos.

"Here she is, Doc." Bob pointed to a large red

and white cow with a huge red thing covered with bumps hanging out below her tail. She was swishing her tail back and forth, staring at us. "Her calf is in the pen next to us, I thought that would keep her calmer."

People started crowding around the pen, leaning over for a better look. "What're those mushroom things?" "How're you ever going to get that back inside of her?" "She doesn't look too happy to me." "It's bleeding and dripping all over." "What's that purple stuff stuck to it?"

The cow's tail swished even faster, and she paced back and forth, splattering blood with each swish. People jumped back as the blood hit them.

"Oh. Gross, these are my church clothes." "She's bleeding to death."

"Bob, I'm going to have to try to rope her from here. She's so worked up I can't get in there with her. Everyone, please be quiet and stand still. You're scaring her."

Dad took his rope and made a loop with his quick release. He leaned over the fence and tossed the rope at her head as she walked by him. She saw the movement and the rope missed as she stopped.

"Doc, I'll rope her." Bob grabbed the rope out of Dad's hands, opened the gate, and stepped into the pen before Dad could say anything. He shook out a loop and started walking toward the cow. She lowered her head, shaking it side to side.

Bob kept walking toward her cooing, "Good Bossy, good Bossy."

"Bob, I would get out of there. She'll take you."

"She'll be ok after I get the rope on her."

The cow charged Bob, and he threw the rope and ran to the side of the pen. He had one foot in the air to step up on the gate when the cow caught him on his rump with her head. She tossed him into the air. He bounced off the wall and landed on a bunch of the relatives. Dad's brow was tight as he rushed over to Bob.

"Bob, are you ok? Is anything hurt?"

Bob stood up. "She's never done anything like that before. Is everyone all right?

Four people stood up, dusting themselves off. One lady held her arm. "I think I sprained my wrist. I'm going to the house. That's enough excitement for me today."

The cow ran around the pen, the rope around her neck. At least Bob had lassoed her, so now all they had to do was grab the rope she was dragging and tie her up. She was trying to get out of any crack she could see daylight out of. She stepped on the rope and it jerked herself to a stop, twisting her neck around. She kept trying to force her nose through the top half of the door to the outside. She pushed one final time, and it gave with a pop. The cow leaned on the door, stretching her neck over the top. Crack. The bottom half of the door split. She jumped over the rest of the door and headed outside. The rope went snaking along, and then the knot in the end of the rope caught in a V formed by the broken wood. The remaining door flexed out, and the cow bellowed as she hit the end of the rope and stretched it to its limit. The door held. Dad immediately ran outside the way we had come in, and I followed him.

"Stay here, Ray. I'm going to get my spare rope. Bob, get a tractor. We don't want anyone to get hurt. I'll get another rope on her and tie her to the tractor. I don't know how long the door will hold, and she'll get away to the timber pasture."

The cow continued to fight the rope, weaving in an arc like a fish on a line. The uterus flopped back and forth, slapping her on the hocks. The crowd had come out of the barn now and stood at a safe distance this time. One of them was bent over, throwing up just outside the barn. Someone else was patting them on the back each time they heaved.

Dad came back, and Bob came around the corner on an old red tractor. He stopped, and Dad climbed up on the fender. One of the crowd opened the gate, and they drove into the lot. Bob drove up next to the cow, forcing her closer to the fence. Dad dropped a noose over her head and then climbed off the back of the tractor and looped the rope around a fence post. Then he went down farther and made another loop around a post. Zing! The knot from the first rope came loose from the door and flew out, scaring the cow. She jumped up, and the uterus flopped up and down with a squish. Each time the cow moved closer to the fence, Dad pulled the rope tight until she was snubbed up to the fence post.

"Ray, give me the lidocaine and then go get the halter."

I handed the tote with the lidocaine over to him and then ran back into the barn and picked up the halter. Dad was giving the cow an epidural when I came back. Her tail became limp as it lost feeling. I handed him the halter, and he put it on her and tied it to the post. He then untied the rope to give her some slack and let her breath a little easier. He tied it again in case she got loose from the halter.

"Ray, please give me the bucket now."

I handed the bucket over the fence to him with the really big scary needle, and people started coming up to the fence.

"Folks, stand over to the side. She has been scared enough, and it will be better for her if you stand over there." He pointed dramatically toward the barn.

Everyone started shuffling over to the barn, and I went with them.

One woman asked me, "What're those mushroom things on her uterus?"

"Those are what help feed the calf before it is born. The cleanings attach to them. Dad will take off the cleanings before he puts the uterus back in."

"What's the cleanings?"

"It's the afterbirth. It's attached to the mushroom thingies, and that's what goes to the calf's umbilical cord before it is born. If it doesn't let go then sometimes Dad has to clean a cow."

Dad had his plastic sleeves on and had the uterus washed off. Bob was holding the tail to the side. Dad put his arm under the uterus and lifted it up, letting the weight of it fall against the cow. He pushed parts of it with his free hand and switched arms as he became tired. Everyone stood silently now as sweat ran down Dad's face.

Bob said, "You're getting it Doc. It's a lot smaller now."

The cow strained, and it all came back out, splattering Dad with blood. He picked it up again and soon had the uterus back to where it was before she strained. He gave a final push, and there was a gigantic sucking sound as the uterus slipped back into the cow.

"Good, now I'll make sure the uterus is all right side out," Dad reached into the cow all the way to his shoulder and fished around a little bit. He picked up the Buhner needle and poked it into the cow. She didn't even flinch when he poked it through and then pulled the suture through. She was totally numb from the epidural. Dad poked it through the other side of the vulva, pulled the suture through and started tying the knot. That was hard to watch, but it was different than a needle you gave shots with. I also knew she couldn't feel it.

"Bob, here's where you should cut the stitch in three to four days. I've seen cows get bred even with it in but it is better to cut it out. A lot of these cows will breed back and not have another problem."

Dad stepped back and the cow shook a little, then she started quivering. Dad shook his head in disgust. "She must have torn a blood vessel with the uterus flopping around. The blood vessel was pinched off until the uterus went back in. Then it started bleeding. It's too late to do anything about it."

Bob and the whole crowd watched in horror as the cow went down, gasped a few times, and was still. Everyone crowded up to the fence to look at the dead cow.

"Well, Doc," Bob said with a catch in his voice, "you tried your best, that's all you can do. I'm going to have to get the chute fixed so this doesn't happen again."

"It's just no fun for anyone with something like this. How're you feeling after hitting the wall?"

Bob took off his hat and rubbed his head. "I have a goose egg on my head. I don't even remember hitting my head."

"When you're running for your life, adrenaline keeps you from feeling pain a lot of times. You better get some ice on that and take care of your company. I'll get the ropes and halter. Ray, here's the tote and the bucket."

Dad took the ropes and halter off the cow and coiled them up. Bob turned the tractor around and looped a log chain around the cow's back leg, pulling her out of the lot. The audience trekked back to the house, jabbering about what had happened.

Dad came back to the truck, and he was covered from head to toe with blood. He put the ropes and halter back in the truck and started hosing down his boots and scrubbing them with his brush. He took off his boots and coveralls and put them in the back of his vet box. He took off his shirt and started scrubbing up his shoulders and upper arms.

"Dad, you have some blood on your face."

He handed me a towel he had dried off his arms with. "Here, wipe it off the best you can. Your grandmother will have a fit if I walk in all covered with blood."

I scrubbed his face off the best I could. He pulled a clean shirt out of his truck and put it on. The entire crowd was gone now. Bob had pulled the cow out of the lot. She was at the end of the lane waiting for the rendering works to pick her up. We drove by her as we left, and Dad looked over at the cow and gave a big sigh.

Chapter 10
Snow Queen

Dad and I were out checking the cows to see if any more were calving. "Ray, I've been thinking. You're going to be a calf short to show next year at the county fair. What would you think about flushing Snow Queen so that you can have some more calves to show the next year? We have a few ugly cows that would do a good job of raising a calf."

"Wow, I might have three or four more calves to show!"

"Don't get your hopes too high. I think it's more likely you'll have one or two more to show, if any. It's also a little risky as Snow Queen may not get pregnant this year after the treatments. That's the risk you take with a heifer."

"What do I have to do, Dad?"

"We will give her several injections and then AI or artificially inseminate her. A week later, we'll flush out the embryos—those are the baby calves. Then we'll put them in our other cows. They'll grow in the other cows, and the cows will have them and think they're their own natural calves. If we get too many, we'll freeze the embryos and put them in later or next year. She may not have any, but you don't know until you try. She also may not like us after all of those injections, but we'll use as small of a needle as we can."

"I can handle that, Dad." At least I could handle Dad doing that. I couldn't give a shot to a cow. I might poke myself; Dad could just do it. I'd get out of it somehow.

"Ok, I'll write up the protocol for her and we'll start next week."

Dad set up the schedule so that I would be out of school the days we would AI and flush Snow Queen. The first day we put her in the barn and ran her into the chute with a little feed for bait. She liked that, and the needle was small so it didn't hurt too much. But I couldn't watch when Dad gave the shot. I just scratched her back to distract her. We did the same thing to the other cows the next day.

The next week was the start of a series of shots. "Here, Ray, you can give the first one. She won't mind too much yet."

"I don't want to miss Dad."

"That's ok, since she's a heifer, we have some extra medicine. If you miss then I'll give it." He held out the syringe for me.

I couldn't let Dad see I was scared of needles, so I reached out and took it. I turned toward Snow Queen. I closed my eyes and pulled the cap off of the needle.

"Ouch!"

I had pulled it off and brought my hands back together, stabbing myself. I dropped the syringe.

Dad grabbed my hand. "It isn't bad. It's a good thing you just had your tetanus shot not all that long ago."

"Am I going to turn into a girl from that shot?"

Dad picked up the syringe. "No, you didn't even inject anything since you weren't holding the plunger. I'll get a new needle and give her the injection so you won't bleed all over everything. Here's a clean paper towel. Put some pressure on it for now to keep it from bleeding."

Dad gave the rest of the shots that week, and she didn't like them too much. But at least I didn't have to give them. She snorted and shook her head, all of the time still eating her feed. I talked to her and combed her until she calmed down. I could handle blood and guts, but don't show me a needle.

Finally, the day came to AI her. She was bawling, and the other cows tried mounting her. Dad and I had decided to breed her to Strut. Dad had really liked his calves at the World Beef Expo. Dad pulled a cane out of the nitrogen tank, grabbed a straw, and put it in the water bath to thaw. He gave me a plastic sleeve, pulled the straw out, dried it, cut it, loaded it in the AI gun, and handed it to me.

I walked over to Snow Queen in the chute and put lube on the sleeve. Dad held her tail, and I put my hand with the glove in her rectum and pulled out poop. I kept doing this and it seemed like the poop would never stop coming. Finally, I couldn't reach any more poop. Dad cleaned off everything with a paper towel, and I put the AI gun into Snow Queen. I felt around in the warmness of Snow Queen's insides and found the cervix. I guided the pipette into it, then I started working in through the rings of the cervix. Sweat was dripping onto my glasses so I couldn't see anything, but I couldn't see the inside of Snow Queen anyway. I glanced out of the side of my glasses and saw Dad smiling at me. I kept working, and bump, bump, and nothing, the straw slid ahead and I was through the cervix.

"Got it?" asked Dad.

"Yeah."

"Push the stylette in slowly and don't let the pipette slip out of the cervix."

Something landed on me. Hank the farm cat had jumped onto my shoulder. I reached back to the stylette and felt the pipette slip out of the cervix. "Errrggghhh."

"I'll get him. Did it come back out?"

I nodded.

"Just do it again. It'll be easier this time."

Bump, bump, whoosh, through again. This time I kept my hand on the gun and reached back with my thumb and slowly pushed the stylette until it stopped. I pulled my arm out of Snow Queen. "I did it, didn't I?"

"Yep, not bad for your first time. It's sure easier to learn when you're young. A lot of twelve-year-olds like you do this. Now you have to do it two more times before you are done with her. Normally we only do it once, but she'll have a long heat with all of those eggs being released. I'll pick you up after school tonight, so dress to get dirty. It looks like you'll need a shower before school this morning."

A week later was the big day. Snow Queen was in the chute at the clinic ready to be flushed. Dad had the table next to the chute covered with stuff he was going to use. Maria Hernandez, the student veterinary technician intern, was helping Gladys fill syringes to get ready. Dad clipped the hair above Snow Queen's tail and carefully gave an epidural to numb up her rear end so she couldn't feel what we were going to do. Gladys tied her tail to the side and scrubbed her all nice and clean.

Dad stuck his arm into her and put the catheter in just like he was AI-ing her. "Inflate the cuff, Gladys."

The catheter is a tube with a balloon around the outside of it. Gladys injected some of the flush solution into the catheter until Dad was happy. Dad looked at me. "You get to do the honors,

Ray, since it's your cow. Inject twenty-five milliliters slowly into the catheter. Gladys will run the clamp. There's no needle when you connect it to the tubing."

Did he know?

I attached the syringe to the collection tubing and started injecting. A few small bubbles raced through the tubing, showing everything was flowing. "That's all of it, Dad."

"Ok, Gladys shut off the clamp. Now let me massage the uterus a bit to free up the embryos so they will float around. Ok Gladys, open the clamp, and I'll start working the fluid out of the uterus."

Gladys opened the other clamp and fluid started flowing down the other tube with large chunks of stuff in the collection cup. "That's some good looking mucus, Ray," said Dad. "That's usually a good sign."

"Is that blood?"

"That's normal. Occasionally there are little blood clots."

"Whew, I thought she had infection or was bleeding."

Dad laughed. "There's a lot riding on this, isn't there? Don't worry, what happens, happens. We've done our best, and now it's up to Snow Queen. Let's flush her again. We have to do it several more times plus do the other horn. I can feel several corpora lutea, which is where the eggs came from. I think there'll be several embryos or at least unfertilized eggs."

I heard water dripping. "Dad! The embryos are going all over the floor!"

Dad jerked, startled, but Snow Queen didn't move. "Don't do that to me Ray, the extra flush fluid is draining out through the filter. That way we don't have to look through a liter of solution to find the itty bitty embryos. Let me see if the catheter is in the right place since I moved. Gladys, I think we need to reposition the catheter. Ray, step back a bit and let Gladys help me on this."

Gladys grabbed the stylette and the syringe to puff up the cuff. She started the stylette into the catheter, and then Dad pushed it on in. Gladys released the pressure on the cuff, Dad repositioned the catheter, and Gladys filled the cuff.

"There, no harm done. Let's finish this and see how many calves we just flushed out of Snow Queen."

I put the flushing solution in, and Gladys ran the clamp as Dad milked out the solution. Dad finally pulled out the catheter, and Maria helped Gladys start picking things up. "Let's go see what we have," he said and headed to the laboratory. He turned on the microscope and started looking, slowly moving the collection cup back and forth. He picked up the pipette.

"Did you find one? Did you find one?"

Dad turned. "Don't do that. Now I am going to have to try and find what I thought I saw." He turned and peered through the scope again. He picked up the catheter and worked it around. He opened a Petri dish and put in holding solution. "We have something, but I will look at it later." He looked into the scope and sucked something up with the pipette. He squeezed it into the Petri dish and went back to looking.

I was just dying to know what he had found, but I knew it would just make him mad if I kept bugging him. Then he wouldn't tell me for sure what he had found. Suddenly he turned and gave me "the look" and then peered down at my foot. I had been tapping my toe.

"Go play with Cedrick!"

I picked up Cedrick's fish and drug it around the room with him in hot pursuit. I kept an eye on Dad the whole time though.

Dad kept slowly moving the collection cup back and forth, and I counted five times that he put something in the Petri dish. He sighed, sat back, and rubbed his neck. "Now I'll do it all again to see if I missed any embryos. He slowly moved the collection container back and forth. Now six, now seven, now eight times he had put something in the Petri dish. He stirred everything up and started looking a third time. He moved a little bit more quickly this time, but suddenly he reached over and put something in the Petri dish. He did it one more time, sat back, and threw the collection dish away.

"Let's see what we have. I'll round up those calves in the petri dish and grade them." He put the Petri dish under the scope and started moving the things around with the pipette. "Have a look, Ray. Before you look in the microscope, look in the dish from outside, you can see the embryos glowing in the light."

I threw the fish across the room and looked at the Petri dish. I could see some very small dots glowing in the light going through the Petri dish. I then moved the eyepieces of the microscope closer together and looked through them. There were nine round things sitting together. I focused in a little better and could see they had stuff in them and some looked just alike.

"Look at the top one, Ray. It's an unfertilized egg, the two next to each other are grade II embryos and the other six are grade I embryos. You can see the glow of life in them. You hit the jackpot with eight embryos, that's above average. We have five cows that are at the right stage to put embryos in, and we'll freeze the rest."

"How many calves do you think we'll get?"

"Usually between fifty and sixty percent will get pregnant, so you do the math. Sometimes none and sometimes all will take. Let's start labeling straws and freezing embryos so that we can put embryos in the cows while these are freezing. Gladys will watch the freezer."

Dad showed me how to label the straws, and he started washing the embryos, moving them from one liquid to another to wash stuff off of them.

I had to write very carefully on the small yellow straws. It looked a like a first grader had written on them when I was done, but at least you could read them. Gladys had the freezer set up, and Dad had loaded straws with embryos and put my ID straws on the end of them. Dad put the straws in the freezer and then waited as they cooled. He then had to pull them out and seed them. He would put a piece of metal in liquid nitrogen and then touch the straws. You could see the ice race up the straw as it froze.

"Ok, let's go put embryos in cows."

Dad put an embryo in a cow, and I wrote down which embryo went into which cow and which horn of the uterus he put it in. Good records were important to know whether it was an embryo or an AI calf when Dad ultrasounded later. I opened the head gate, and he ran another cow into the chute and cleaned her rear end up. We finished with all five cows and then cleaned up the chute area.

We went back into the lab, and Gladys was ready for us. "Time to plunge the straws into nitrogen, Dr. Morrison."

Dad quickly took a straw, picked it up out of the freezer, and put it in the nitrogen. He dropped all three of them in and put them in a storage cane. He then put them in the nitrogen tank.

He smiled. "Now you have three calves on ice, Ray. You could keep them there for years and put them in a cow when you are seventy-five if you want."

"Really?"

"Yep, they do it all of the time. Now you'll have to watch the cows in a couple of weeks and see if any of them come into heat on time. If they come into heat, then they aren't pregnant."

Three days later, Snow Queen came into heat, and we AI-ed her to Strut too.

Two weeks later I watched morning and evening to see if any of the cows came into heat. Two weeks passed and nothing came into heat so I was hoping for five calves. Then a few days later, 38, the old black cow, came into heat. Her heat detection patch on her back had been scratched off and turned orange. The other cows rode her every time she stood still. Dad AI-ed her to a show bull. That way Mary or I could have something to show at the fair in two years.

"Ray, we'll ultrasound them later to make sure they're pregnant. We can even tell if it's going to be a bull or heifer if we do it at the right time."

"Wow, four more American British White Parks plus Snow Queens's calf too."

"Don't count your calves before they're born. All kinds of things can happen yet. It's always amazing that anything is ever born, since there are so many things that can go wrong."

Chapter 11
The Preceptors

Sue called back to Dad, "Dr. May, from the university, is on the phone for you."

Dad went back to his office to talk on the phone and soon called out, "Gladys, Dr. May wants to know if we can take a student preceptor for the summer. Do you think we can handle both a vet student and a vet tech student at the same time?"

Gladys walked over to his office and leaned against the doorframe. "I guess it would be nice to have some extra hands around here when Sue and I take vacation. Tell him we'll do it."

Dad came out of his office a few minutes later. "She'll start next Monday and we'll have her for eight weeks. Gladys, I'll have her work with you and Maria some so she knows what to do at your end. She needs to know how to do everything, especially after hours when a technician's not always available. How much longer will Maria be here?"

"We'll have her for another six weeks, then she's going to the emergency clinic for the rest of her summer."

Maria, a small dark-haired girl in scrubs, had been at the clinic for two weeks already. She had a stethoscope around her neck with bandage scissors and a thermometer in her pocket. She was following Gladys around the clinic like an eager puppy. She leaned over the microscope and her hair fell onto the slide with the fecal sample on it.

Gladys smiled. "I think you might want to wear your hair up."

The girl whirled around. "I have poop on my hair? Oh gross. Give me something to wipe it off."

Gladys handed her a paper towel, and she started running her hair through a fold of it. "I'm going to have to wash my hair as soon as I get home."

"Did you see anything on the slide?"

"I thought I saw a worm egg."

Gladys took her time. "What kind of worm egg?"

"I don't know, a worm egg."

"Find it again and show it to me."

Maria bent over the microscope again, holding her hair to the side. "Here it is. Where's a rubber band or something I can use?"

"Ray, would you please get Maria a rubber band while I look at this."

I went over to the drawer of office supplies and brought back a couple of rubber bands. "Which one do you want?"

Maria gave me a quick smile. "This one should work. Thanks Ray. I know your little sister Mary. I was her reading buddy in school a year ago. She told me all about you."

"You can't believe everything you hear from Mary. She likes to make a big story out of everything."

"I think she's cute and just likes her older brother and sister. She told me all about Cy, your Labrador, and your cows. I already knew your dad since I was little and we brought my dog to the clinic. That's why I wanted to work here."

Gladys looked over her shoulder. "Maria, is this the worm egg you saw?"

Maria went and bent over the microscope. "Yes, that's it. It was a little different than I remember seeing in class, but it looks like a worm egg to me."

"Take a closer look at it. Does it look like Mickey Mouse?"

"Yeah, sort of, I can see the ears."

"That's pollen, and we see it a lot. You don't want to deworm a cat for having pollen."

Maria looked up, her face red. "I'm sorry, I thought it was a worm egg."

"That's ok. That's why you're here. We all learned a lot when we did internships. Now you know what it is, and since you were wrong, you are more likely to remember it the next time you see it. You're now a member of the fecal Mickey Mouse Club."

Gladys started to sing then. "M-I-C-K-E-Y M-O-U-S-E Mickey Mouse."

Maria and I just looked at each other. Adults could be so goofy at times.

That night at supper I told what had happened to Maria, the hair on the microscope slide and Mickey Mouse.

Mary didn't think it was too funny. "You're just mean. Maria is really nice and was my reading buddy. She helped me with Spanish."

"That's good to know, Mary," said Dad and smiled. "I knew she could speak Spanish since she has interpreted for her parents at the clinic for several years now. Her parents understand more than they can speak, and she has really been a help when they come in. I think it'll be nice having her there to interpret. She understands more of what we are doing and that should be quite helpful. Ray, I doubt if Maria will make that mistake again. You often remember your mistakes more than the things you do right."

"The clinic is going to be crowded with a vet student coming on Monday as well. I hope I have room to turn around."

Monday morning I didn't have school and a tall, red-haired woman wearing green bib overalls with a caduceus and boots in her arms came into the clinic. "Hi, I'm Diana Smith. I'm here for my preceptorship with Dr. Morrison."

"Nice to meet you," said Sue. "I'm Sue, and this

is Ray, Dr. Morrison's son. Ray please take Diana back to your dad."

"He's back working cattle at the chute. I came up to get some more vaccine. It's back this way."

I opened the door to the garage and the smell of cow manure immediately washed over us. A calf bawled in the chute. I took Diana around to the front of the chute. "Dad, this's Diana Smith. She's here for her preceptorship."

Dad nodded. "Nice to meet you. Go ahead and get your boots on, and we'll finish up."

Dad let the calf out of the chute and shut the gate behind it. The farmer shooed the next calf into the chute, and Dad caught it. "Here Diana, you can vaccinate the calves. Here's the syringe, have you done it before?"

"Yes, I've helped Doc McBride a lot at home," she said and expertly injected the calf.

The calves quickly went through the chute as they were green-tagged. The tag showed they had been castrated, dehorned if they needed it, vaccinated, dewormed, and poured for lice and or grubs. They were also supposed to be weaned, but they needed a paper signed by Dad and the owner to prove everything had been done.

We finished the calves and loaded them onto the trailer for the ride home.

"Ray, can you clean up while I show Diana around?"

"Sure, Dad." I grabbed a shovel and started

scooping manure into buckets. I carried the buckets of cow manure out to the compost pile behind the clinic and dumped the buckets onto the pile. Green manure flecked with bits of corn oozed down to the corners of the heap. It was strong smelling, and I could also smell the rotting manure. Mom would come down later and use this on her garden. Composted cow manure's always in demand by gardeners. I went back in and hosed all the rest of the manure into the pit and turned on the fan to dry out the pens.

Laughter came from the lab. Diana was talking to Dad, Gladys, and Maria. They were talking about fecals and Mickey Mouse ears.

"Hey," Gladys gave me the evil eye, "don't track into my nice clean lab. I just cleaned up the mess your dad made."

I quickly stepped back into the garage and took off my boots. I had washed them with the hose, but they were still wet and left footprints.

Gladys gave me an approving nod as I came back in and wiped up my footprints with a paper towel.

"How about we get a litter of farm cats for you to spay and neuter for practice? We won't charge for them as it would be good experience for you and Maria," Dad said to Diana.

"That would be great, Dr. Morrison. I've done a few surgeries, but it takes me a while."

"Gladys, why don't you see if our resident cat lady, Judy Reece, has any she wants spayed or neutered for free. She'll find some if she doesn't have any of her own."

The next week a thin, little gray-haired lady came into the clinic. "Would someone please help me carry in my cats?"

Sue said, "Ray, help Maria bring the cats in."

Maria and I followed her out to her car. It was an old, old, rusty Ford Ltd with holes in the side so large you could throw a cat through them. She opened the back door, and a wave of tomcat urine odor smacked me in the nose and then ran to the back of my throat making me want to throw up my breakfast. Maria was holding her nose and turning her head. Three half grown kittens in a live trap were urinating and defecating all over the back seat of the car as they clung to the sides of the cage, squalling at the top of their lungs.

"They're a bit wild. I didn't dare bring them in my regular car." Mrs. Reece smiled. "So I brought the cat mobile. I can't get the smell out of it so this's the only thing it's good for."

Maria nodded at the cage. "Ray, you pull it out, and I'll grab the back of it."

I pulled the cage out and that really started a ruckus.

Maria jerked her hand away. "Ouch! It scratched me! I'm going to go get the welding gloves since there's no other way to hold it." Maria stomped off and jerked open the door to the clinic.

Judy Reece just said, "Now, now, you need to

be nicer, Smokey. They're just trying to help you. I had such a terrible time getting them into the trap. I didn't have anything else that would work for Bumpkins there. He just wouldn't let me catch him any other way."

Maria came back with the thick welding gloves. "Ray, you carry it where they can't reach you. I'll carry it by the corners."

I picked up one end of the cage, and Maria took the other end. I heard claws grabbing the gloves as Judy Reece held the door open for us. Urine dribbled out of the cage, and Maria stepped in it. Sue grabbed a mop and followed us back. Cedrick sniffed and poked his nose into the whole procedure.

Gladys eyed the kittens. "Ray, put Cedrick away, he's causing too many problems. Maria, you're going to have fun with them. Do you have your dart gun ready?"

"Dart gun?"

"How else are you going to be able to handle them? If you open that trap door then they'll probably make a run for it when you least expect it. We'll see what your 'doctor of the day' wants to do with them."

Diana Smith came back. "Wow, this should be fun. Maria, do you think you can get one out, and I'll do a physical on it before surgery? I can draw blood and run a panel."

"I don't think I can get one out for all that. They're

loco and scared to death. Ask Dr. Morrison what you should do."

Dad came back and leaned against the wall, surveying the situation. "It looks like you two have your job cut out for you. You're not going to be able to do a physical or blood work on these cats. I would estimate their weight and give them an injection through the cage, then you can pull them out one at a time as they are sedated. Gladys will help you." He smiled and walked out.

Gladys pulled out the sedative and gave Diana a syringe. "Here you go. They're all yours."

"Maria, how much do you think the gray one weighs?" asked Diana.

"I think it weighs about four and a half pounds."

Diana wrote in the file and started calculating dosages for the drugs and then went and checked with Dad to see if they were ok. She came back, picked up the vial that Gladys had set down for her to use, and inserted the needle. She pulled up the dose and tapped the syringe to get rid of the bubbles. She bent down and quickly poked the gray kitten sitting in the corner of the cage.

"Got him!" the kitten jumped and hissed at her.

Maria bustled around, getting ready for surgery while Diana watched the kitten. The kitten started to look very sleepy and then it started moving and making urping sounds. "Aaaaaack," the kitten vomited a big pile of food on the bottom of the cage. White worms squirmed in the pile of puke.

"I guess we need to deworm these kittens then," said Diana. "What can we give them while they're asleep?"

"The only one we can give them while they're asleep is a topical, but it's expensive. Since we're doing these for free, I doubt if Dr. Morrison will want to spend that much," said Gladys with a twinkle in her eye. "You'll have to squirt it in their mouths after they wake up."

"Uh, I don't think I can do that without them biting," said Diana. "They're just too wild to handle."

"I'm just kidding. We'll send something home to put in their food or let Judy give it to them at home. I think the kitten is ready for the second injection. Let's pull it out and weigh it so we can give a more accurate dose of anesthetic. Maria, hold the door up while Diana uses the small loop to pull the kitten out."

The two kittens that were not sedated scrambled to the back of the cage as Maria held the trap door open on the cage. Diana took the small pig snare and snagged a back leg on the sedated kitten, quickly pulling it out of the cage. Maria let the door slam shut. The kitten slowly rolled over, and Maria wrapped it in a towel and took it away to weigh it.

Maria came back with the kitten. "Four point six pounds."

Diana quickly figured her dose, checked with

Dad again, and injected the kitten, who faintly hissed at her. Maria put it in a cage to finish going to sleep and then went in to make sure the surgery was ready. Maria came back a few minutes later and checked to see if the kitten was completely out and took it to prep it for surgery. It was a girl, and Maria started shaving its belly.

Diana came in holding her arms up, dripping water from her elbows. She was gloved up and ready to go as Maria finished scrubbing the cat. The cat was soon draped, and Diana was ready to make her incision. Diana made her incision, and it was really small. She fished around for the uterus with a spay hook.

"I can't find the uterus, all I keep getting is omentum and intestine," said Diana as she stuffed intestine back into the incision.

She kept working at it, fishing around and pulling parts out. She was starting to sweat and had Maria wipe her forehead so it wouldn't drip into her eyes or onto the cat. She made the incision longer and fished around some more. Now it was long enough she could put her finger into it. Omentum, intestine, and bladder all came out, but no uterus.

"There, I think this is it," she pulled out a narrow pink strand. "Call Dr. Morrison and let him see if I am right."

I went after Dad, and he came into the surgery. "Let's see what you have there. Hmmm, I think you have a ureter. Don't pull any harder, take a quick look and let it go. Here, you have been at it a while, let me put on some gloves and give a quick hand."

Dad put on his surgery gloves and Diana handed him the spay hook. He put the spay hook in the cat and then kind of looked at the ceiling while he fished around. He pulled out the spay hook and a pink narrow tube was on it.

"There, it's just something that takes practice. Here ya go, I'll let you finish up." Dad snapped off his gloves and left the surgery.

I followed him out. "Dad, why don't you stay there for the whole surgery?"

"I've found out that it makes the students nervous if I'm looking over their shoulder the entire time. I'm right here so if there's a problem I can help out. I can also get some paperwork done and see patients while they're doing surgery."

Maria was cleaning up the surgery while Diana drew up the sedative for the next cat. Diana bent over the cage to give the injection and quickly popped the needle into the kitten. It gave a big yowl and jumped. The sedative squirted into the air, and the kitten cowered at the other end of the cage.

Diana was exasperated. "What am I going to do now? Some of the sedative went into the cat and some didn't. Dr. Morrison. Dr. Morrison!"

Dad came running. "What do you need?"

"The cat jumped when I was giving the injection and some squirted out. What should I do now?"

"How much do you think went in, any at all?"

"Some did, but I don't know how much."

"Let's wait, and see how the cat acts. If you gave any, we'll see some effects in a few minutes. If nothing happens in five to six minutes, we'll start from scratch. If it starts getting drowsy, we'll play it by ear," Dad said and went back to his office.

Five minutes later, "Urp, urp, urp, aaaaacccccckkkk." A pile of food was on the bottom of the cage, but the kitten didn't seem as out of it as the other one had been.

Diana looked at me. "Ray, will you go get your dad and tell him it threw up?"

Dad came back with me. "Let's see how sedate you are." The kitten looked up at him groggily. "I think you can give the next injection, we'll give a little bit more of the sedative at the same time."

Maria held the cage door open again, and Diana soon had the sedated kitten snared and pulled to the open door of the cage. It was fighting some, and Maria had the towel in her other hand, ready to cover it up as soon it was out of the cage. The cat decided it didn't want to come out and hooked the bottom of the cage with its claws. Maria reached in with the towel and covered it, working its paws loose. Diana held the cage door open while Maria used both hands to hold onto the cat. The other cat at the back of the cage saw the door open and bolted for freedom.

Dad slammed the door to the room shut. The cat went around and around trying to get away. It jumped up on the counters, knocking stuff all over the place and then up on the top cabinets, yowling in fear the entire time. Maria was still holding onto a squirming, sedated cat.

Dad cracked open the door. "Gladys, bring the fishnet! Diana, give the second injection to the one Maria is holding. We'll use gas for the rest of the surgery."

Maria uncovered a leg, and Diana quickly injected the cat. Maria put it in a cage, and then it was up to us to catch the other cat that was now cowering on top of the cabinets. Gladys had slipped the fishnet through the door, and Dad now brandished the net as he edged near the cat.

Dad slowly raised the net and put it over the cat. The cat was so high up that he could not get the net flat on top of the cabinet and as he pulled it toward the edge, the cat slipped out of the net and jumped down. It ran around the room, jumping up and knocking things over every time it came to a wall or corner. Dad, after several attempts, scooped it up and quickly flipped the net over so the cat was dangling over the edge.

"Here you go, Ray, cat on a stick. I'm afraid to let it go since we have to do surgery on the other cat. Can you hold it here and talk nicely to it to calm it down while Maria and Diana get the other cat ready for surgery?"

"Sure, Dad."

Dad laid the handle on the counter with the kitten hanging over the edge. I just had to lean on the handle to keep it there. The kitten tried to pull its head in and hide from me even though there was no hiding in the fishnet. Dad came back in and hung a towel over the net to make the kitten feel more secure.

"Nice kitty, nice kitty, don't be scared." The cat just stared balefully at me through a gap in a fold of the towel. I kept talking to it the whole time they were prepping the other cat, and it gradually relaxed a little bit. I heard the clippers going and the cat in the net pulled its head back into its neck like a turtle into its shell. I just kept talking. "Nice kitty, you're just scared. I just want to be your friend."

I could see through the window in the door, and Diana was prepping for her second surgery of the day. Gladys helped Maria with the anesthetic machine. I could see Diana marking out where her incision was going to be when she cut into the cat. She fished around again with the spay hook. She pulled something out and stuffed it back in.

I was starting to get tired when Gladys came out and said, "Dr. Morrison, would you please come back?"

Dad came back and stood in the door. "How're you doing?"

"I have something here, and I know it's not

another ureter. I can't find the uterus, but have found everything else. I can't figure out what this is."

Dad leaned over, glanced at it, and then reached under the drapes and felt around, "What you have there is the vas deferens. Congratulations! You have officially spayed your first tomcat."

Diana's face flushed. "I forgot to check in all the excitement and assumed Maria looked. Please don't tell my professors," she pleaded.

"I won't, but a lot of veterinarians have done what you just did, myself included. Now, suture your incision and we'll get this tomcat prepped for surgery."

Diana sutured away, then Maria and Gladys soon had the cat ready for the next surgery. Dad and I weighed the other cat and soon had it sedated as Diana finished up. The last cat was another tomcat, and Diana didn't spay this one.

Acknowledgements

I dedicate this book to my wife Lana, and our four children: Seth, Jared, Kenan, and Sarah. I want to thank Dr. Dick and Joyce Jaspers for my first position as a veterinarian and the care they showed me then and still. Author Roxanne Rustand encouraged me to do something with this book one way or another, and I appreciate her encouragement. Many people have read this and given me encouragement over the years before it was published. A special thanks to Doug and Linda Corpman for the proofreading, encouragement, and ideas for this book.

My clients and their animals over the years have enriched our lives. A classmate told me that clients are more than just a client, they are friends. That has been demonstrated over and over during my years of practice.

Amie McCracken, my editor, rode with her dad. This is the story of her life and others who were the child of a veterinarian. They know so much about what a veterinarian's life is like.

Thank you to Robin Vuchnich for the cover design.

About the Author

Dr. Ninja is a mixed animal practioner in Iowa. He works on a little bit of everything except skunks. He raises American British White Cattle with two of his sons. He is an inventor, occasional speaker at continuing education for veterinarians, hunter's education instructor, elder in his church, and now writer. He has been a youth sports coach, garbage truck worker, detassled corn, worked construction, raised Labradors, and many other things.

Links of interest from the book

Thistledown Farms LLC
www.tdfarmsllc.com

American British White Park Cattle
www.whitecattle.com

Percheron Horse Association of America
www.percheronhorse.org

Bulldog Club of America
www.bulldogclubofamerica.org

The National Beagle Club of America, Inc.
www.nationalbeagleclub.org